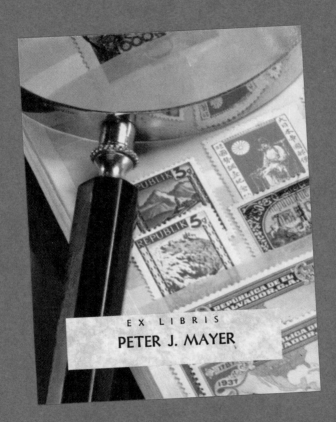

CAESAR'S

GALLIC
WAR

CAESAR'S

Houghton Mifflin Company Boston

GALLIC WAR

Olivia Coolidge

The Riverside Press Cambridge / 1 9 6 1

Books by Olivia Coolidge

GREEK MYTHS

LEGENDS OF THE NORTH

THE TROJAN WAR

EGYPTIAN ADVENTURES

CROMWELL'S HEAD

ROMAN PEOPLE

WINSTON CHURCHILL AND THE STORY OF TWO WORLD WARS

CAESAR'S GALLIC WAR

The decorations in this book have been adapted from old engravings supplied by Culver Service and The Bettman Archive.

CONTENTS

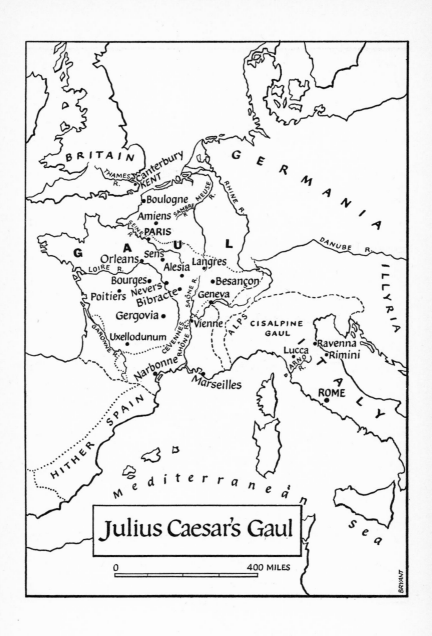

Julius Caesar's Gaul

0   400 MILES

BRYANT

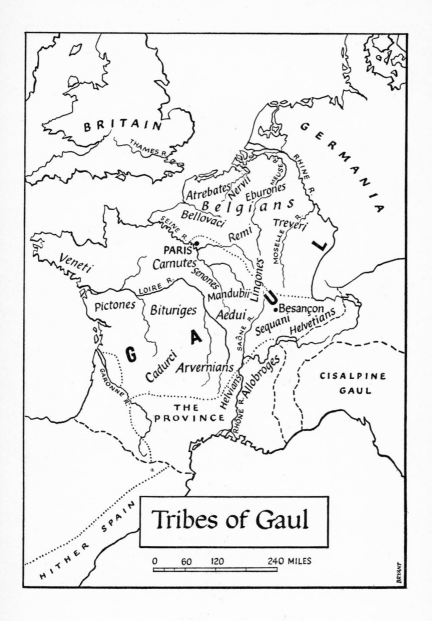

Tribes of Gaul

BRITAIN

GERMANIA

THAMES R.

RHINE R.

Atrebates

Nervii

Eburones

MEUSE R.

Belgians

Bellovaci

SEINE R.

Remi

Treveri

L

Veneti

PARIS

Carnutes

Senones

Mandubii

Lingones

MOSELLE R.

U

Besançon

Pictones

LOIRE R.

Bituriges

Aedui

Sequani

Helvetians

G

A

SAÔNE R.

GARONNE R.

Cadurci

Arvernians

Helvetians

Allobroges

CISALPINE
GAUL

THE
PROVINCE

RHONE R.

HITHER SPAIN

0   60   120   240 MILES

BRYANT

INTRODUCTION

CAESAR's *Commentaries on the Gallic War* are among the most interesting historical books which the Romans have left us. It is not often that a commander of Caesar's fame has the ability to write well. His firsthand account, written in an extraordinarily simple, clear style, gives us a picture of the Gallic War which may be taken from the Roman point of view, but which is real. Reading Caesar, we know what he knows — how the Gallic War actually was.

Unhappily, though all this is true enough, it does seem probable that Caesar's book has bored a larger number of children than any other book in the Western World. This is hardly Caesar's fault. He did not write it for beginners in Latin, or for people who do not know one Gallic tribe from another and do not care. In fact, he did not write it for children at all. Times have changed.

Fashions also change with the times. On reading Caesar today, we are bound to be struck by the fact that he did not approach the problem of writing an account of this war from the angle that we would prefer. In these days of newspapers, for instance, we are used to reporting. We expect stories. We want to know about the common soldier, who he was and what he felt. We like pictures of people, places, weapons, clothes. We demand photographs, if not in literal fact, at least in the form of vivid description. Now the Romans, who had to get their news from common gossip or from letters, wanted facts.

Caesar gave them exactly that. Indeed, he packed his *Commentaries* so full of facts that we, who do not know the background, may well find them hard to digest. Caesar treats his characters less as people than as agents, appearing only when they are doing something that needs to be mentioned. Diviciacus, for instance, was a Gaul with whom Caesar had a personal friendship. During the first years of the war, Diviciacus is a man without whom Caesar can do nothing. Then suddenly he is not spoken of again. Other people lead his tribe, and it is perfectly clear that Diviciacus must be dead. Caesar, however, keeps strictly to his subject and does not say so.

In this way people move in and out of Caesar's book with startling abruptness. Caesar's officers come for a year or two and go again. He never comments or describes them in any way. They are there, and then not there. Caesar is also conscious of being the commanding general, and though he narrates many acts of bravery, he feels the need of doing so with restraint. It would be favoritism to mention one man too often. Nor does he think it proper to speak of individuals below the rank of centurion at all. No doubt it would have caused offense in the higher ranks if he did.

All these qualities make Caesar's book rather more than less forcible, but they explain why people in our day often do not enjoy it. It is only when we put it together with all we know from other sources about the Gauls, about individual Romans, their political background, their army training, and countless other things that we perceive how greatly Caesar has enriched us. The object of writing a new book on the Gallic War is not therefore to summarize Caesar, but to add to Caesar's story a great deal which he left out. It is hardly possible to do this without writing some fiction. Most of the characters are real ones. Some, however, like little Varus, are invented to show types. Others, like old Caburus, are real enough, but have a fictional background. Conversations and scenes where they take place are imagined ones which may make a personality vivid or give information.

The narrator, Octavius, is a shadowy figure who is used for firsthand descriptions. To make him more vivid might mean that his adventures became more important than the real characters. As a young officer with a slight literary talent, he is typical, too. As an admirer of Caesar, he is able to paint us the same sort of picture Caesar did. No doubt a Gaul would give us another side, but this is Caesar's war.

I have used the modern French names for towns, where these

still exist, rather than the Roman ones. French names are generally shorter and more familiar; besides, they can be found in any good atlas. At the end, there is a list of these names and their Roman equivalents. A few towns are either so famous in their Roman form or so obscure today that is has seemed better to use Caesar's own name for them. Gergovia and Alesia are samples of such names.

To sum up, this book is a mixture of fact and fiction, a modern presentation of the war Caesar was writing about, limited by our knowledge, but drawing on the resources of archeology and classical research. It is not a translation, but perhaps a companion to Caesar — a help to those who have to read him and are not able to perceive that he is not dull.

Prologue

The Book of Quintus Octavius

I was one of Caesar's officers, and being connected by marriage with his niece, I was for a while attached to his staff and knew him well. In writing of his war in Gaul, I do not attempt to rival his own story, but rather to illustrate it somewhat after a fashion he once suggested to me. The year in which he was with us in winter quarters, he passed the evening with us from time to time in general discussion. We were talking once of how history was written when Caesar threw out the notion that I might give color to a war such as ours by piecing together the experiences of a few chosen people or by bringing characters to life. It

was instinctive with Caesar to express ideas, but he had no intention of using this one for himself. His masterly work is conceived of as the product of a great commander-in-chief, concerned with stating the facts precisely and clearly. Yet he took an interest in my scheme because it pleased him to fire younger men with inspiration. As it happened, however, the worst years of the war were yet to follow. I was busy thereafter both summer and winter alike, so that apart from talking with people I knew, I accomplished little.

I might have let the idea drop. It was my fortune in the last siege of the war, at Uxellodunum, to receive a spear thrust that nearly ended my life. Indeed, in a sense it did do so. My soldiering was over, and the great civil wars which followed at once were fought without me. All the people who had been my friends in Gaul died fighting in them or were killed in the butcheries that went with them. I only survived because I was crippled and ill and obscure. I wish I had died.

I have lived on these thirty years, health broken, advancement at an end, all purpose lost. I have become nothing but a tiresome bore whose very stories about the last war but two or three are out of date. I had never forgotten what Caesar had suggested, yet somehow the effort of looking for survivors seemed very great. I might never have done it had I not run unexpectedly into a little soldier I once knew. His name was Varus.

I recognized him at once. He had lost a couple of fingers from his sword hand. His nose was broken, and there was a scar down one side of his face which puckered his cheek. He limped and had grown bald from the rubbing of his helmet. He still had, however, a trick of whistling through his teeth, and the tune was an old one we used to hear in Gaul. "Why, Varus!" I said.

He looked up at me with his head on one side as he used to do, but he did not know me. "I was with Caesar in Spain and Africa and Greece," he said. "Then with Aulus Hirtius when he was killed by Mutina. It was fighting with Octavian against young Sextus Pompey that I lost these." He held out his hand. "Couldn't hold a sword rightly after that, so I set up in business with this inn and a string of post horses. There's many that pass by here that I know. If you could give me so much as a hint . . ."

"It was further back than all that," I said. "It was in Gaul."

"That's a long time ago." He squinted up at me again

in despair. "Great days those were in Gaul — the greatest. A long time ago."

I knew I was terribly altered and it was not fair. "Do
you remember Octavius," I said, "the young military
tribune who was going to put your adventures into a
book?"

He remembered at once and smacked his hand on the
rump of my near horse, roaring with laughter. He never
had believed me about the book, had thought I was jesting,
and seemed to have no trouble in finding it funny.

"I never did write it," I said. "It was all too confusing. We didn't see the war as a whole."

To my surprise he answered soberly. "Don't read myself," he said. "Never learned. But my boy reads, and he
reads me what Caesar wrote. Makes it clear what we were
all doing."

He meant to advise me with the naïveté of the ignorant
to read Caesar, which he evidently thought I might not
have heard of. Suddenly, however, two things came together in my mind — the old ambition to write a new
sort of book, and the perfect clarity with which Caesar had
described the course of the war. I had been attempting to
write what Caesar had been compelled to leave out. I

should have included also what he had written. The combination might not be the literature I once had aspired to, yet it represented the best years of my life. I said to Varus, "I never did write that book yet, but now I will."

I

THE DELIVERER

58 B.C.

1

I shall start my book with The Three, for it was from the rivalry between Pompey, Caesar, and Crassus that this war sprang and reached its final dimensions. Ambition for power in Rome impelled Caesar to grasp his opportunity in Gaul. With the help of Philo, who was Caesar's secretary and slave, I have put together a picture of these three men on that great day when war really began. Then too, Publius Crassus, whom I loved best of all the men who fought for Caesar, told me something of his father and himself. My family connections with Caesar made the tale of Julia, his daughter, Pompey's wife, familiar to me. Marcus Cicero was but a pawn in these great affairs, but the story of his life belongs to history, and I write of nothing new there. His fortunes and those of his brother were intertwined with Caesar's, for which reason I speak of him briefly now. These bits and pieces together make up my tale.

CAESAR drove north from Rome, and he drove in a
hurry. It was not that he urged his coachman unneces-
sarily. Rather he sat back against his padded cushion,
allowing the driver to make the most of every undulation
in varying the pace of his horses. Yet when they broke
into a fast trot and the carriage lurched behind them,
jolting up and down on the straps which served as springs,
he answered a quick look with a nod of his head and
said, "Only another two miles in this stage. Don't spare
us now." Behind him the tempo of his escort's horses
accelerated also, outdistancing with every yard the lum-
bering baggage, which had fallen miles behind and would
most certainly not be seen in the next two weeks.

The Aemilian Way was a remarkable road, fourteen
feet wide and paved with blocks of basalt. It ran up the
coast through the plain of Tuscany, uncompromisingly

straight where it could be so, ignoring the curves of the coast line. Only here and there was the sea very close, though almost always it could be seen somewhere on the left, a distant line — not the brilliant blue of the Mediterranean in summer, but its uncertain gray in March. Spring was coming, was indeed here. Trees had broken out in greenish-yellow blossoms. Peasants were plowing. Skylarks flooded the air with song, and the uncertain bleat of lambs drifted across green fields. All the same, the weather was raw. Driver and passenger sat muffled to the eyes in heavy cloaks, one brown, the other scarlet. Leather curtains which ran round the light carriage on a rail were drawn across the right side to give protection from the wind. These comforts, however, of cushion and curtain and cloak could do very little to protect their owner from jolting or from the penetrating rain of spring, which seemed to threaten.

The escort consisted of a second, two-wheeled carriage in which a groom drove me. I was twenty and raw enough to feel strange in my officer's white cloak. Four men on horseback rode behind, two of them common soldiers, and two secretarial slaves of the better class. These last were looking anxiously at the sky, while exchanging comments on whether we would reach the posting house before the rain came down. Luck held. We all went clattering down a long and gradual slope to draw up steaming — eight men needing eight fresh horses and a chance to stretch their legs or take refreshment.

The posting house consisted of a dingy inn or bar flanked by large stables. These latter were built round a courtyard which at this time of year was deep in stinking mud. Luckily, however, there was a paved entrance court where the horses could be unharnessed and led to their empty stalls across a causeway of bundles of rushes not yet quite as dirty as the surrounding earth. Shock-headed slaves swarmed out to do this chore, while the proprietor, an elderly ex-soldier with a white scar down one cheek, appeared in the door of the inn to offer greetings.

Officious and very young, I jumped to the ground and wasted no time on being polite. "On the business of the Senate and People of Rome," I snapped. "Caius Julius Caesar, Governor of Illyria and of Gaul, both on this side of the Alps and also beyond, is on his way to his province. He requires your best eight horses without delay."

The innkeeper threw out both hands in a helpless gesture and broke into a torrent of speech from which the uncomfortable fact emerged that he had not eight horses available at this time . . . not eight fresh horses that was. He would requisition them. Let Primus go without delay . . . "At once, at once, Primus!" . . . But it would take time, there being no other horses, literally none in this poor village . . . only oxen and maybe an ass or two. He called the gods to witness that if he had known the proconsul was to pass on official business . . . on so traveled a road and in mud season . . . Did not the noble officer understand?

The noble officer did not. Having started by demanding the impossible in the name of the Senate and People, I was led by zeal to add threats. These did not by any means fail of effect, since the innkeeper knew it was his duty to assist the proconsul with all he had, and free of charge. He tore his hair, gestured at his children, beat his breast, and even brought tears to his eyes with floods of eloquence. But he did not have eight horses . . . "In a short hour . . ."

"How many horses could you make ready at once?" Caesar had dropped a fold of his scarlet cloak to ask the question in a quietly pleasant tone which made no apology for his aide's bullying, yet did not endorse it. His unexpected calmness brought results. With a reasonable minimum of explanation and excuse, the innkeeper admitted to five . . . and another which needed shoeing, which was already being shod, which was — he would stake his life on it — a good horse, only needing . . .

"Then we must make do with the six." Caesar crooked a beckoning finger for my groom. "You take the first horse and ride on ahead to the next stage that there may be no further delay. Meanwhile, I have letters to write while this shoe is put on. Philo may stay to take them back to Rome as soon as he can be mounted. You, Velleius, may wait behind with Philo and carry my instructions to the legions in Aquileia."

All was suddenly settled. The host reverted to his natural self and swore at his stablemen without more ado. Philo extracted from his saddlebags the wax-covered wooden tablets used for letter-writing. I stood by, frowning at the dark sky while I struggled with a feeling which I had met before in Caesar's company — a sense of having handled something in a very clumsy way. The little problem appeared so perfectly simple now Caesar had solved it.

Caesar himself looked up at the sky and shivered. "It's starting to rain." He glanced dubiously at the inn, whose tiny windows exuded not only smoke but a powerful odor of bad stew. A board outside it advertised a Syrian dancing-girl as the attraction. The notice, I reflected, had been there a very long time by its looks. That girl most probably was a bent old crone by now. These pub-

lic hostelries were all pretty much alike and all flea-
ridden.

"Best stay dry as long as we can." Caesar stood up in
his carriage with sudden decision, sweeping the cloak
back over his shoulders as he jumped to the ground with
the agility of a younger man. Caesar at this particular
time was forty-three. He was wiry and slender, moder-
ately tall for a Roman, five feet nine inches, perhaps. He
moved with grace and was in fact a famous horseman,
though his general appearance was fragile rather than
athletic. In emergencies, however, he made demands on
his physique which only exceptional determination and
force could have endured. This very journey was to
mean pounding over the road to Further Gaul from dawn
to dark in all weathers, and day after day. His mounted
escort could not endure the pace and had to be exchanged
before passing the Alps, where even the maritime road
was full of brigands. Arrived in his further province, Caesar had immediately to march with a single legion to con-
tain a gathering horde of more than a quarter of a million,
a nation on the move whose way must be barred.

As he jumped to the ground with his back turned for
the moment, Caesar had looked young. His face, however, corrected the impression. For one thing, his dark
hair was already receding fast. For another, that lean,
lined, aquiline face can never have looked natural on a
boy or a young man. To see Caesar in an unguarded moment was to fancy that he had been born old. Yet as he
came over to me where I stood in that dirty courtyard
cursing my own loutishness, his dark eyes twinkled and
his mouth curved into the smile which had long been
famous as the most charming smile in Rome. Caesar took
me by the arm and nodding at the hostel inquired in a

tone of mock outrage which reminded one of the dandy he had been, "Shall we face it together?"

Philo reached the suburbs of Rome with Caesar's letters at about noon the next day. He left his mule there for convenience's sake. It was far easier to traverse the narrow streets of Rome on foot, especially during the day when the little shops pushed out their wares and their customers into the roadway. By the time he came to the house of Crassus, public business was over. The Senate, angry and helpless, had met without even discussing the matter which was on its mind. The common people, that is to say the political gang which held power for the moment, had met under its boss, a tribune of the people, and had passed an outrageous law. Thereafter both Senate and people had dispersed to their homes or their business, seething with gossip. The rich went to their baths and dined at leisure, and the poor to their particular business, begging, hawking, stealing, or carousing in some dive on political handouts which were circulating at this time from some source one did not mention.

In the house of Crassus, Philo readily noticed this tendency to conceal the source of wealth. It looked from the outside like a large block of shops with dwellings above them. It was only by walking around that one discovered what a huge area this enclosed. In fact, the modest entrance led to a labyrinth of courtyards, reception rooms, banquet halls, or private suites, all decorated with beautiful paintings or faced at vast expense with imported marble. It was a house with no imperfections. Quiet servants, speaking only when spoken to, effaced themselves around corners, patiently waiting to wipe up what had been spilled, replace what was shattered, snip off

what was faded. So vast were their numbers that no corner of that house was ever private. No physical effort
of stretching out a hand or writing a note was ever demanded of the owner against his will — no effort of
memory even. There were special slaves to remember,
slaves to write, and slaves to tell time. All Crassus needed
to do of his own accord was to eat or sleep. If he did not
care to walk, he would be carried.

Strangely enough, the owner of all this wealth, Marcus
Crassus, was by no means a soft man sunk in luxury. He
tended to use it merely to save wasting his energies in a
way that was not good business. Perhaps for this reason
he was a hard man to his slaves, demanding perfection as
a proper return for his investment in them. Throughout
his life, his success in making money had led him to eval-
uate people in monetary terms. To this rule, however,
there were two exceptions. Crassus genuinely loved his
sons. His ambitions for them were worldly in the extreme, and his methods of promoting his interest or theirs
were those of a none-too-scrupulous business tycoon.
His love, however, was perfectly free from these taints,
and he was apt to feel distress whenever his children
protested against his actions.

Young Publius Crassus was protesting now. He and
his father were walking around a pool which had been
surrounded overnight by masses of scented violets. The
servants lurking in the pillared porticoes were not out of
hearing, but with the indifference of habit, neither man
cared.

"So great a genius!" young Publius exclaimed. "The
savior of his country! How can we treat him so?"

The older man grunted and hunched his shoulders
slightly. Seen thus together, the likeness between the

two, though great, was less startling than their difference
of expression. Marcus Crassus was by now in his middle
fifties, but looked older. He was squarely built and stout-
ish, hard-faced, with a dogged chin, a mouth like a trap,
and piercing little black eyes. His son Publius was built
after much the same model. Short, sturdy, and athletic
with very massive shoulders, he carried himself like a soldier. In the shape of his face and his coloring he resem-
bled his father; but whereas Marcus looked out on the
world with shrewd suspicion, Publius loved it. He had
a touch of the quality which makes great leaders of men,
a noble eagerness to bring out the best in others. Even in
his twenties, his staid or cynical elders in Rome felt
strange affection for Publius, no matter what their party.

"That you should consent to this!" he said again.

Marcus turned round on him sharply. "Who mentioned my name?"

"Your money talks," the young man remarked. They
walked in silence.

"You know my bargain with Caesar," Crassus said at
last. "We had him made consul last year, and he introduced measures to get us out of that quite ruinous con-
tract and to settle Pompey's veterans on farms. These
things had to be done and Caesar did them—never mind
how he did them in spite of his colleague, that fool Bibu-
lus. The Senate could have done them itself, had our conservatives more sense. Government is for settling such
problems, and not for pursuing party grudges. But all
these fools thought of was a chance to upset our measures
as soon as Caesar was out of the way in Gaul. Don't
imagine that we wanted to be forced to teach them a
lesson."

"I understand," the young man said. "Indeed I do.

But the conservatives have their own point of view. They do not like to be ruled by The Three — and indeed if I may say so without offense to you, Father, none of us do. It was always the glory of the Roman Republic that power was in the hands of the whole body of citizens, not of any few. Times have changed. I bear no malice toward Caesar, and as you know I am eager to serve beneath him in Gaul. Yet if it is necessary to bolster his power and yours and Pompey's by forcing into exile the ornament of our age, the one man who opposes your measures from conviction rather than party, may I not question the justice of The Three? And can you defend it?"

Marcus Crassus grunted again and kept his eyes on his feet. He was far from wishing to disillusion his son by crass exposure of the real facts of his life. Nevertheless, he must defend his own actions, and he brooded a moment over how much he should say.

"That Cicero's a fool," he said bluntly, deciding on attack. "He may be the ornament of our age; he may have splendid convictions; he may be a genius for all I care. He's still a fool. By birth he's a small-town politician from nowhere, and it still shows. His impossible ideals! Had he been brought up in a great house where politics were common talk from childhood, we might be able to make him see reason now. As it is, he forces us to drive him out of Rome for fear of his heading a party to destroy us all. I made no attack on Cicero myself, and I don't like the way it was done. To exile a man who has saved us from armed revolution on the pretext that at a time of crisis and with the Senate's full consent he put some guilty citizens to death — why, that's ungrateful, shameful even. I didn't vote for it. I didn't set the tribune on — though mind you it had to be done. What's Caesar waiting outside the city for when he ought to have been in his province ever since the first of the year? Caesar knows there's trouble brewing across the Alps and that he's risking a defeat with every week he stays. Yet he daren't turn his back on Rome with Cicero in it. He offered the fellow a place on his personal staff, and was refused. Can you blame him for taking the speediest way to drive Cicero out of Rome?"

"With the help of your money," young Publius said, his eyes on his feet.

"I don't," retorted his father, "dictate how the money's to be spent. That's part of my bargain."

This was specious, and both knew it. But it touched far too nearly on the real point at issue between them, which was that the elder Crassus saw politics in terms of bribery, while the younger clung to ideals. Because of the affection between them, neither wanted to admit this difference, but preferred to walk in silence. When they had made the round three times without a word, one of the servants detached himself from the portico sufficiently to be seen without intruding. Receiving a curt nod from his master, he then spoke.

"There is a man here, sir, with a letter from Caesar he would like to deliver himself."

"Bring him in."

Philo made his appearance and stood waiting while Crassus broke open the tablets, which had been tied with thread and sealed with Caesar's seal. He scanned them hastily and turned to Publius. "This concerns you. The Helvetian nation, which has been threatening for two years to migrate to southern Gaul, is on the move. Their leaders have fixed the twenty-fourth of March for an

assembly of the people by Geneva. All their villages are
to go up in flames, and when they are ready, they will
move across the Rhone into our province. On hearing
these tidings, Caesar left within the hour. He'll never get
there in time to stop that horde."

"He will," young Publius said, "because he must."

His father smiled at him fondly. "You would have
done so! But Caesar is not so young. And only yester-
day was Cicero forced out of Rome! I told you there
was urgency in that matter."

Publius had made his protest and would not quarrel
with his father. He said, "I'd best give my orders and be
off. I'll be needed in Gaul."

"Your baggage should be starting at least," Crassus
agreed. "I'll tell the steward to put fifty men onto getting it out of Rome tonight. But I don't like you racing
off. There'll be confusion in the Province for a while.
Best let it settle." It was in his mind that if Caesar were
going to suffer a bloody defeat, young Publius had better
not be in a hurry. Publius, however, merely grinned.

"I'll let it settle for a few hours anyway. I start tomorrow."

Philo left Rome by the southern gate and picked up a
mount in the outskirts after haggling for almost an hour
with one of the sharp horse dealers who preyed on trav-
elers around that popular exit. Gnaius Pompey was at
one of his country villas about a day's journey from Rome
— a convenient distance for watching over what went
on without appearing to have any part in it. For Pompey
had been a friend of Cicero, who had always hoped to
persuade him to put his power at the disposal of the
Senate. This Pompey might have done, for he personally

disliked Crassus and was a conservative at heart. All he wanted was to be the foremost citizen of Rome, her greatest general, the man who had made or put down kings, who had carved up the East as he saw fit, and without whom no war would be successful. In fact, Pompey did not precisely want to rule, but to be deferred to.

Had the leaders of the senatorial party perceived this, and had they recognized Pompey's obligations to his own ex-soldiers, it seems possible that the alliance of The Three would never have come into being. Probably Pompey might already slightly regret that it had done so. Its price to him had been high. Backing Caesar as consul, he had seen the law rewarding his veterans pushed through by highhanded methods which were in themselves a shock to the authority of the Senate, which Pompey respected. He had stood by also while Caesar had grabbed the appointment to the provinces of Gaul, where war threatened. Not that Pompey expected Caesar to win great glory in Gaul. Why should he? Yet if Caesar did win glory, Pompey would be jealous.

The affair of Cicero's exile had been worst of all. For Cicero had appealed to Pompey, who had more or less promised to protect him. What else could he have done for a personal friend? Yet in the event it proved impractical to allow the outraged Senate to take its revenge by undoing Caesar's measures as soon as his back was turned. If an example was made of their most prominent man, they could be quelled. Pompey really had no option but to sacrifice his friend and break his word. Hence the country villa, the pretense of semi-retirement, while his followers made common cause with those of Caesar and Crassus in Rome.

Philo found Pompey talking with his friends. There

were plenty of people who thought it necessary to keep in with Pompey by driving out to see him every week, always hoping for an invitation to dinner or to spend the night. Not only was the villa itself always thronged, but the owners of neighboring villas came in for the overflow, while the local tavern, unpleasant though it was, did a roaring trade.

Pompey looked at the letter in silence, saying nothing of the contents. He was quite a handsome man, only two years older than Caesar, which considering the part that he had played was extraordinarily young. His manner was courteous, but condescending. He expected deference; and while he read Caesar's letter and thought for a moment over what he should do, the company sat in silence. Presently he nodded at Philo. "Go, take some refreshment. I will consider my answer," and so he dismissed him. Then turning to his friends with no more ceremony, he simply informed them that he had business and calmly left them.

He found his wife among her friends, who — being suitable to her own age — were of a different generation. His own son, Sextus, for instance, was sitting laughing at something Julia had just said. People usually did laugh at what Julia said, and Pompey, who had no sort of wit of his own, was enchanted by hers. He smiled at her, and she leaped to her feet, scattering a mirror, a bunch of violets, a gold pin, and a new poem which she happened to have on her lap.

"I must beg you to excuse me," she said to her group. "When Pompey comes to seek me in person, and in the afternoon, too, it is an event."

The remark was quite simply made as a statement of fact. Pompey was important in Julia's eyes, and his some-

what regal air seemed perfectly natural in a husband two
years older than Julia's father.

"I wish to show Julia a letter," Pompey said.

Her little group took the hint and made their adieux.
Julia trod on the poem, picked it up, and gave it back to
the author with rueful apologies. Someone else picked
up the violets, and Julia dropped them again. There was
more laughter. Pompey regarded the little scene indul-
gently. He was not in a hurry, and if it had ever crossed
his mind that Julia laughed more readily with others than
with himself, her unselfconsciousness would have reassured him.

Julia said her last goodbye and turned to Pompey a
little flushed and sparkling. In such moments, her likeness to Caesar was extraordinary, though luckily for her-
self she had not inherited his high-bridged nose or
worldly, cynical air. "A letter?" she inquired. "From
my father?"

Pompey nodded. "Come and read it." Julia leaned
against him to read it over his shoulder.

"That's serious!" she said, aghast. "Can Caesar possibly arrive in Further Gaul in time? And when he gets
there, with only one legion and the other three this side
of the Alps, what can he do?"

"Never worry," Pompey said firmly. "That's only
what these barbarians think they will do. There's bound
to be delay, and your father will manage."

Julia put her head against his shoulder for a second and
sighed with relief. "That's all right then."

"Of course it is," Pompey insisted. This was what he
had come to say, and he said it stoutly, though in point
of fact it was not his opinion. Caesar's military experience
had not been very great — a little fighting in an amateur

way in the East at a very young age, and a small campaign against hill tribes in Spain which had been managed, to do Caesar justice, perfectly well. Pompey rather imagined that Caesar was about to find out that leading an army was not quite the same as playing politics so successfully in Rome. Deep down in his heart, moreover, Pompey was anxious to have Caesar learn such a lesson. The exile of Cicero had been very painful, and Pompey felt sore. He patted Julia.

"I wanted to show you the letter first," he said, "so that I could assure you that you need not be alarmed."

Julia took him quite at the world's valuation. "It was good of you to think of me," she told him. "I shall not worry at all, since you tell me not. You know."

Pompey thought he did.

A man drove south from Rome, and he drove slowly in a big four-wheeled coach encumbered with baggage. An elderly slave rode with him, and all about him on the seats were packed his books in neat leather rolls. Behind him, a creaking cart bore luggage and slaves. They had already been two days on the road and had not progressed much more than fifty miles. Cicero sat with his head on his hand all day unless the sound of hurrying hoofs was heard behind. Then indeed he would look round with painful expectation, while the slaves on the cart stared back uneasily too — none of them knowing whether news, if it were to come, would be good or bad. Some sixteen years from now, Cicero was to meet his death at the hands of pursuers from Rome, and under the eyes of some of these very slaves. They did not precisely fear his death now, and yet in these tumultuous days one never knew. But he would not hurry.

The cortege halted in a little town in Latium for the purpose of changing the horses. Cicero would not get out and expose himself to curious eyes. He preferred to sit in the semi-dark with the curtains drawn and hide his misery. Somewhere his servants found the text of the bill which had been passed in Rome by the mob. After consultation, his elderly slave went up and gave it to him; for now the worst was known, and they must be gone. Cicero read it and groaned as the tears poured down his cheeks. His servants, who loved him, had tears in their own eyes. The carriage went on again, a little faster.

2
THE SAVING OF THE PROVINCE

Insofar as it is anyone's story, this chapter is the tale of old Caburus, who represents in my mind the Gauls already under our rule in that southern part which we used to call the Province. Caburus was utterly loyal, despite his connections of blood and friendship with many of the free Gauls. He made for us the greatest sacrifice possible — both of his sons. I was acquainted with the older one, Procillus, who was interpreter for Caesar. Through him I understood in part those Gauls who were already Roman, who served willingly against their brothers in blood, but who were reluctant to do what they saw they must do. Thus even as victors these men were not exempt from the tragedy of this war. Its profit was Caesar's.

ON THE MORNING of the third day, Caesar crossed into Lucca. There is no visible frontier save the Arno between Roman Italy and Italian Gaul. Yet I say advisedly "crossed," for within a mile one senses the difference. Nearer Gaul has been ours for over a hundred and fifty years. It is dotted with colonies of Roman veterans, while Roman traders have pushed up along the great roads and established themselves everywhere. The very natives are by no means all of them Gauls, but are often Etruscans, Ligurians, and other Italian races who were conquered when Gauls swept down past the Alps, three hundred and fifty years ago, to be finally halted and penned in the north of Italy by Rome. Gauls themselves cut their hair short, shave, and wear Roman dress for the most part. They speak Latin. Yet there is a difference.

The people themselves stand out, for one thing. When

one gets to know Gauls, one perceives they are not all tall, blue-eyed, and red-haired. However, one's earliest impression invariably is that they are, for the type is common, and one often sees a trace of it in people who are in fact brown-haired. Their brown is lighter than ours and frequently has an auburn tinge. It goes with gray or hazel eyes instead of brown or black. Their skin is fairer. They wear Roman dress, as I said; and yet occasionally one may see a peasant plowing in a tunic and loose trousers, or an old man sitting in the sun with long white drooping mustaches and hair straggling down his back. Such older people do not by any means always speak Latin, while the peasant speaks it indifferently as yet. So far only the townsfolk use it at home.

Their love of bright colors stands out everywhere. It is only the poor people who wear their plaid cloaks now, and these are usually faded and dirty. The garish splendor of a rich Gallic chief from Long-haired Gaul is not seen this side of the Alps. Yet the plaids, dingy as they are, are still more colorful than our Italian brown. The brooches that fasten them are of ornate workmanship with twists and spirals in original designs. The more elaborate are decorated, too, with red enamel.

As with the people, so with the houses. Towns of any size are sure to be Italian, but the cottages of the poor are as they have always been, while the farmhouses are typically Gallic with their hall, their narrow passage running all along one side, and their communicating rooms and outbuildings. Their roofs, too, are peaked and bear no resemblance to ours.

The other change, which came very suddenly as we crossed into Lucca, was the change in the position of Caesar. In Italy, he had been a proconsul on business for the state. In Gaul, he was Governor. This meant deputations at every posting house, ceremonious invitations to spend the night, improvised banquets, petitions, queues of people paying respects. Caesar's genius for business, which was very great, included the ability to cut an interview off without offense and to make decisions fast. Never had he needed these qualities more; yet though his determination pushed us on at ninety miles a day, even he could by no means manage to get much sleep at night. I can call to mind those banquets still, impossible to refuse and endless to sit through. Next morning Caesar would have himself strapped to his seat, lest he roll off it and out into the road while he was sleeping. Very occasionally when we made good time, he would have his attendants draw up by a deserted stretch where he could rest for an hour under a tree. This happened seldom, for the foothills of the Apennines came down to the sea just here as they prepared to join the Alps, and the road was harder.

Gaius Valerius Caburus, a chief of the Helvians, was a singularly lucky man in a difficult age. He had been born plain Caburus at a time when the Roman occupation of the extreme south of Gaul, though a fact, was hardly yet a final one. Caburus had taken kindly to Roman civilization, since he happened to be one of those intelligent barbarians to whom higher culture makes an appeal. The Helvians, moreover, had been a small tribe and always bullied by their neighbors to north and south, the powerful Arverni and the ambitious Allobroges. The Romans had conquered the Allobroges, who lay in the path of their desire to link up Italy with their provinces in Spain by a land route. In the fighting which brought this about, the Romans also had smashed the power of the Arverni. Caburus and the Helvians in general found themselves freer as a part of the Province than before. Their loss of independence was more than compensated for by protection from their neighbors.

It did not follow that the Roman administration of their new province of Further Gaul was entirely perfect. There were good governors and bad. Indeed, the state of chaos into which Roman politics had fallen rather tended to produce very bad ones. Caburus, however, had endured the worst and still remained loyal, even though the Allobroges had risen in revolt a few years back.

His rewards had been proportional to his service. He had taken the title of Gaius Valerius when a Roman general of that name had granted him Roman citizenship, which was possessed by very few Gauls. Moreover, the spoils of campaigning on the successful side had certainly enriched him with far more than Roman extortion had ever wrung out of him in taxes. Besides his vast Helvian estates, Caburus now possessed a series of farms among the Allobroges and a town house built in Italian style in their city of Vienne on the Rhone, where he was now. Instead of being a chief among other chiefs of an obscure tribe, he was one of the greatest persons in the entire province, not only on account of his wealth, but because of his friendship with Romans of all sorts, whom he entertained lavishly at Vienne.

In appearance Caburus was a tall, slight man, rather dark for a Gaul. On receiving Roman citizenship, he had cut off his long hair and trimmed his mustaches, compromising by growing an iron-gray beard, somewhat after the fashion of the Greeks, with whom he was acquainted through their great colony of Marseille. By this arrangement, Caburus was able without looking odd to wear his Gallic costume on his estates and the toga in Vienne. The compromise was typical of his position. Though he could not himself read Greek, he had sent both his sons to Marseille to school. Later on, the elder had spent a year in Rome, where Caburus himself had visited him. The younger, however, was harder to control.

"Where is your brother now?" he said to Procillus angrily. "With our whole province in an uproar this last month, with Caesar here in the nick of time and demanding a levy, is this a moment for Dumnotaurus to disappear without a word? Where has he gone?"

Gaius Valerius Procillus was dark, too; and with his cropped hair and shaven face he might have passed for a Roman, save for his light gray eyes and long, narrow head. He spoke three languages, but Latin for choice, preferred Vienne to the country, and the Roman colony of Narbonne to them both. He shrugged off Dumnotaurus almost angrily. "He has gone to our cousins for the festival of the spring equinox. He has ambitions, as I think, to become a Druid."

Caburus snorted, inarticulate with real annoyance, as much with Procillus for the flippancy of his tone as with his younger son for being absent. The rites and traditions of the Gallic world were no less real in Caburus's eyes because he also happened to admire things Roman. It was not the festival of the equinox which angered him now, nor even the suggestion that Dumnotaurus might desire to learn the magic of the Druid priests. It was the cousins.

"Must he go among the Arverni? Could he not have kindled the magic fire on our own estates? He knows I cannot leave Vienne before Caesar comes."

"The Arverni have the Sacred Mountain," Procillus said.

"What has that to do with the equinox? It is young Vercingetorix whom your brother goes to visit. Sooner or later this Vercingetorix will conspire to make himself king over the Arverni, as his father once did. He will be put to death as his father was, and Dumnotaurus no doubt with him, though I have warned him often. If Dumnotaurus desires to be a great chief in Long-haired Gaul, he had far better go to Britain and study with the Druids."

"Vercingetorix is a born leader," Procillus remarked. "He may succeed."

Caburus made an impatient gesture with his arm. "Young Vercingetorix is marked for death. All the elders have set their spies on him. He will not grow old. What do the Arverni need with a king? If they try to recover their former glory, they will stir up trouble which the Romans will never forget. Can Vercingetorix turn back the years merely by being uncommonly handsome, a great hunter, a lavish giver, and popular with foolish young men? I thought you at least had more sense."

"Perhaps it is that I do not care who rules the Arverni," said Procillus lightly. "They are not of the Province. You know Caesar spoke to me a year ago in Rome and promised me I should be his interpreter to the Gauls? He'll need me at Geneva."

If Caburus felt some of the reluctance of old Marcus Crassus in Rome, he did not show it. Danger was the proper business of a chief, and Caburus was ambitious for the future of his sons. To have Caesar's ear might be important. "Caesar spoke of it to me as well," Caburus agreed. "Is your gear ready?"

The town of Geneva lies on the lake of that name where the river Rhone flows out at its eastern end. The Rhone is a swift-flowing river, deep and exceedingly blue. I remember watching how a shallower stream joins it right by its source, the latter carrying gray, chalky-looking mud, as Alpine streams do. Those two colors flowed side by side down the Rhone and hardly mingled until they went round a bend and were lost to view. I remember wondering if blood in that clear, blue water would do the same.

When Caesar arrived on the south bank of the Rhone, the Helvetians on the opposite side were mustering still. Their total numbers, according to their own count, were three hundred and sixty-eight thousand. Very likely each chief exaggerated the numbers he brought, and each village likewise. But however this may be, their host was vast. To try to count their campfires at night was like counting the stars in the sky. By day the noise of them was a continuous roar. Their encampment was by no means opposite ours, but down by the Lake of Geneva; and therefore the lowing of oxen, the creaking of carts, the hammering, yelling of children, and a thousand other sounds were blended by distance into one muttering tone which never altered till night silenced it. Our Roman forces were but a single legion, four thousand five hundred men in actual strength. Auxiliary levies from the Province, mostly cavalry, came straggling in.

The Helvetians did not hurry. When they perceived that Caesar was with us, which they easily could from observing the commander's tent, from hearing his trumpets, or from seeing his scarlet cloak, they sent envoys. These came deliberately riding to the water's edge and took boat, two chiefs and their escorts. Very splendid they looked to the eyes of those of us who were new to Long-haired Gaul, most strange and savage. One wore red, green, and gold, the other a rainbow of colors. Both had torques of beaten gold about their necks, the ends of them fashioned into heads of beasts with brilliant scarlet eyes. Their brooches, too, were of gold, while the buckles of their swordbelts and their long scabbards were of bronze, very curiously engraved. What with their huge weapons, mighty frames, and long hair which they had treated, as Gauls will sometimes do, with lime to make it stand out behind almost like a horse's mane, these chiefs were really figures at which we stared in awe. Their followers behind them were dirtier and wilder, possibly chosen as guards on account of their size. Even Caesar, who was fairly tall, as I have said, was dwarfed beside them.

Caesar met them outside his camp on a knoll from which a wide view of the river could be seen, its banks on our side unfortified and entirely bare of defenders. There was a stretch of the Rhone some twenty miles long which could quite easily be crossed by a bridge of boats wherever the banks were low. Beyond that point the mountains called the Jura came down to meet the stream and close that path. So far, all Caesar had done was to break down the bridge by Geneva. This, however, could not stop the host from pouring over the river almost at will where it was not defended.

All this the Helvetians saw — the unprotected bank, the tiny camp, the single legion. Their information about us must have been confirmed at a glance, and their swaggering manner gained in assurance. Each of their chiefs stepped forward to make a speech in that queer, harsh language, Procillus translating.

The gist of their argument was that they wished to leave their country because it was hemmed in by mountains and lake, and they had outgrown it. Furthermore, they admitted the Germans were pressing them from the northeast. For both these reasons they had agreed to move and had sent emissaries to various tribes in Gaul two years ago. They had now decided to settle in southern Gaul near the Atlantic and the mouth of the Garonne. In order to do so, they must pass out of their present territory by the one route fit for their wagons, that by Geneva and over the Rhone into the Province. They were ready to take an oath not to plunder there and would offer hostages. Caesar for his part must guarantee to let them go through unmolested.

There could be no question in Caesar's mind of allowing the Helvetians to pass through the Roman province. For one thing, one might as well try to dam up the sea as to stop that host from plunder. For another, the Helvetians were not the first barbarian nation whom Rome had seen on the march. The Cimbri and Teutons fifty years before had done the same, had wandered in Gaul for a while, pretending to settle first here, then there, and had finally marched on the Province. They had defeated the consuls. They had threatened Italy. Rome never forgot them, and Caesar would not have dared to let the Helvetians loose in Gaul. With the situation in Rome as dubious as it was, to have done so might have cost The Three their power and Caesar his province.

Naturally Caesar did not disclose his mind. Had he done so, the Helvetians would have attacked the crossings at once and must have gained them. He nodded and appeared to consider. The barbarians, as he knew, were by no means ready to move. Their farthest canton was straggling in, and the smoke of their villages still rose upon the air. It would suit them well, if they thought themselves safe, to waste more time. Caesar told them with a fine nonchalance that he wished to consult the chiefs of the Province. He therefore suggested that they come back on the ninth of April, when he would give them their answer.

There was a very long moment while the envoys spoke together. Caesar appeared quite at ease, while Procillus managed to whisper to someone and laugh. The rest of us quite frankly held our breaths. On that moment hung the future of the Province, of Caesar, and of ourselves. The ninth of April was a carefully thought-out date, just far enough away to seem reasonable, considering that the chiefs of the Province could be no closer than Vienne. It was also just near enough to make it impossible for Caesar to call up help from Gaul — yet far enough away, he thought, for blocking the river.

The two chiefs fell headlong into the trap, took ceremonious leave of Caesar, who escorted them to their boats, and so departed. Hardly had they turned their backs before Caesar set all of us to work without wasting an hour or a man. He had already gone up and down the riverbank with his engineers, had marked where the cliffs would protect it and what earthworks would be needed. He had even had the men told off, so many to fortify each crossing place; and he had already issued rations to those who would be farthest off.

Our men toiled till they dropped. Most luckily it happened that the main part of that twenty-mile bank was very steep and needed nothing save mounted pickets on the watch, lest daring spirits should try to scale it by night and come round on our fortifications from behind. To hold the crossing places which could have been bridged for their wagons, Caesar relied on a ditch and a rampart, the latter sixteen feet high and studded with forts. He placed his catapults as best he could to sweep the bank, while manning each strong point as lightly as he dared, so that reinforcements might march wherever they were needed.

The Gauls do not understand the science of fortification, save where they have learned it from us. Their warriors consider it beneath them, save in the last resort, to use a spade. The Helvetians therefore held off, though they must partly have seen what we did and could if they cared have seen more. On the ninth of April, their envoys came swaggering back to receive our surrender. Receiving instead Caesar's flat refusal to let them pass, they were far more angry than dismayed, despite the panorama of our works which Caesar permitted them to view. They laughed at our numbers, threatened to take what they would, and went back to their people.

Now followed a week of sleepless nights and desperate struggles. The Helvetians lashed boats together, made rafts, even forded the river in one or two spots where it runs broad and shallow. They came by night, attempting surprise. They came by day. They tried to overwhelm us by their numbers and their sheer fury — in vain. There must have been much blood in the Rhone, but I never saw it there. My eyes were on the barbarian casting his bundle of fagots into our ditch, climbing on the shoulders of his fellow to thrust with his long spear, or planting his ladder on the bodies of his dead. Still more often it was pitch-dark, even raining. Torches sizzled out. Here and there our men would throw over balls of rags soaked in grease which they had set afire. The mass of locked shields would quiver, and open, and drop it

through. Then our people would pelt the men whom
they dimly saw with darts or stones. Perhaps the gap
would widen until in a panic the barbarians fled back to
their boats, or tried to swim and drowned in the dark.
Perhaps a group of them would find their way onto the
rampart where each man fought in his own little circle
of vision which reached for a very few yards. The
blackness which had helped them get thus far prevented
their fellows from seeing what they had done. Fierce
wrestling matches took place where Roman and Gaul
toppled together into the ditch and there were trampled
till they drowned in mud and water. Somehow the rampart was always cleared again and the barbarians broken.

There were dead men in the Rhone washed up on every
headland. Our soldiers left them alone, save where they
offended their nostrils or where the corpse of a chieftain
promised plunder. At the most they pushed them out into
the stream for the next headland, on whichsoever side it
be, to intercept them. Helvetians, however, when a kinsman was dead went searching the banks and sometimes
risked swimming over. The noise of their jabbering and
the lamentations of their women rung in our ears.

They desisted at last. For twenty-four hours there
was no attack, and every man had his turn to sleep. Their
warrior parties moved away from the bank and back to
the encampment of their nation by the lake. Caesar's Gallic spies, who traded very freely, brought back the news
that they were asking the Sequani for permission to pass
through the Jura. The route which led this way was very
narrow and could easily have been blocked. The Helvetians, however, had friends among the Sequani, who were
not unwilling to let loose this vast horde upon the territories of the Aedui, their enemies and neighbors.

Caesar perceived that though he had saved the Province from invasion for a while, there would be war in Gaul. So huge a displacement of people would set the tribes at each other's throats. Some would join the Helvetians, increasing the size of the moving mass. Others, dispossessed by them, would seek their fortunes elsewhere. In this turmoil the Province must sooner or later be involved. Caesar was not disposed to sit and wait for trouble. He had already ordered a levy of two fresh legions in his province of Nearer Gaul across the Alps, where he had three veteran legions in winter quarters. While the Helvetians were getting under way and defiling slowly through the mountain pass of the Jura, Caesar determined to return to North Italy as swiftly as he had come, to make all arrangements there, and to march back with his five legions. Snow was melting in the passes of the Alps, and he would take a shorter route. Labienus, his lieutenant, a soldier much admired though seldom loved, would hold the line of Geneva, lest the Helvetians after all turn back this way.

3

CAESAR'S LEGIONS

Little Varus was a friend of mine, insofar as an officer may make a friend of a legionary soldier. In our army we did not deal with the men, but gave our orders to centurions and heads of smaller detachments. We nearly always respected our centurions, but disliked them. We could but admire Sextius Baculus, for instance; yet I wonder if anyone cared for so savage a brute. There was nothing that Baculus would not dare, and he typifies for me the unconquerable spirit of our legions. Little Varus took his tone from such people. Varus would swagger and boast with the best. He could be bloodthirsty and brutal. Yet under it all he remained an unspoiled peasant who expected life to be hard and who gave or took knocks with good-humor. To put it otherwise, he came of the stock which breeds great armies. It was Varus and his kind after all who conquered Gaul.

I<small>T WAS</small> more than fifty years before this time that the tribes of the Cimbri and Teutons were first known to be migrating. Some suppose that pressure from the far north had driven them southward; others say an earthquake and a tidal wave had ruined their land. Whatever the reason, these tribes had started to wander with their wives, their children, and their cattle — seeking as they said a place to settle, but far more evidently living on plunder. The Romans, who had from the first been concerned to head them off from Roman territories, were thrice defeated in the following six years. Gathering forces for a fourth attempt, the consul Mallius was killed at Arausio in Further Gaul with a loss of eighty thousand men. There seemed no reason why these barbarians should not pour down through the Alps. A panic swept Rome.

Rome turned to her greatest soldier, Caius Marius. It happened, however, that the fault lay less with her generals than with her army. The Roman soldier who had conquered Italy, Carthage, and Greece had been a citizen farmer, serving at his own cost and supplying his arms. But the more the Roman dominions spread, the more impossible it became to ship men home at the end of a season. Campaigns of several years became the rule. Pay was introduced, but this in itself scarcely solved the problem, which was that neglected farms were going to ruin. Morale went also. Peasant soldiers were in no way bred to arms or taught how to use them. As armies became larger and maneuvers more elaborate, simple courage was not sufficient, even where it still existed.

Rome needed a crisis and a bold, uninhibited man to find a solution for these evils, which had grown slowly. Such a man was Marius, of obscure parentage and with a talent for only one thing, the profession of arms. Elected consul for five years in succession for the purpose of raising and training an army to beat the barbarians, Marius destroyed the Cimbri and Teutons in two enormous battles, one in the Province and one actually on our side of the Alps in Nearer Gaul.

Tremendous was the relief in Rome. Great was the rejoicing. However, when this wore off, Caius Marius and his army remained, each one a problem of a new sort to the state. Instead of the army of old, this army consisted of poor men, landless men, second sons, adventurers. It had enlisted in part for the pay and in hope of plunder, but largely because Marius had promised that after they had served a term of years, the state would give each man a farm to retire to. For the fulfillment of this they looked to Marius, and only through him to the state. In this way Marius ushered in the age of revolutions which has plagued us ever since. Other men have been quick to learn. Every war requiring an army has produced its own general and its demands. Statesmen have observed that to become powerful in Rome, they must first win a war. Generals have turned their armies against each other. Even Caesar at this moment of crisis in Gaul was hardly thinking of the Helvetians, but of his position in Rome and of The Three. Pompey had an army. Crassus had wealth. So far Caesar merely had brains, which did not suffice.

This personal interest in war was common to Caesar and to the whole of his army, right down to his youngest recruit, little Titus Varus, who was actually fifteen, though he said he was older. He was a small farmer's son and had run away from home to escape his brute of a father. He had no trade of his own, and unskilled labor was performed everywhere by slaves. Young Varus had therefore the choice of drifting to Rome to scrounge a living as the hanger-on of some political gang, or of joining the army. The latter held greater risks, but far greater prospects. Varus was lucky in that Caesar's lieutenant in Nearer Gaul was holding a levy to raise two additional legions, while it happened that the border of Nearer Gaul was but fifty miles north of his father's holding. Varus became a soldier with the dizzying prospect before him of rising from the ranks some day to be centurion, of retiring in middle life to a farm of his own with a nest egg and a few slaves, of affording to marry, of attaining possibly the magistracy of some small town, or being able to boast of twenty years of glorious adventure. All these visions depended first on victory, then on Caesar.

It is true that Varus found the life hard. His centurion, one Sextius Baculus, was a brute as his father had been. Baculus carried a stick which he could apply with terrifying force. It was necessary to placate him with little gifts from one's meager pay, which was not easy because this was docked from the start for one's equipment. Varus, however, shared Baculus's attentions with very nearly a hundred other raw recruits in a raw legion of almost six thousand men. Companionship in itself made life seem pleasant. All discovered much at the same time that the hobnailed military boot blistered their feet until the leather was softened by hours of rubbing with grease. All felt the leather corselet chafe their bodies, the sword swing against their legs, the helmet grow heavy and hot. The leather shield with its metal rim was not only awkward but appeared to weigh a ton, and for the present their centurion would not permit these to be loaded on the carts. Full equipment was carried on every practice march, and this included two heavy javelins, two stakes, an entrenching pickaxe, and sixteen days' full rations. Varus was hardy and used to working from dawn to dark, but he ached in every limb and slept like a log.

There was so much to learn. It seemed that after a lifetime spent in working on the land, he did not even know how to dig. The speed with which old soldiers threw up entrenchments made him gasp. He had to practice cutting and thrusting with his sword at a post, or throwing javelins at a man-sized mound of turf. Then there was maneuvering. He must have six feet to fight in by himself, no more and no less. He must press forward into the front line only through a gap. He must be able to advance in an unbroken line over rocks, brush, or ditches, to wheel or retire in formation. Above everything, he must at all times and in all places know where he belonged. He was tenth man in the second century of the eighth cohort. As such, his position in the battle line of the legion was fixed, his tent was pitched in exactly the same spot in every camp site. The very pack horse which carried his tent and the mill to grind his corn were always the same ones and always followed the line of march in the same order.

This and much more was explained to Varus and driven in hastily by blows. There was little time for practice. The very centurions of the legion were mostly new to their trade, having been promoted from the ranks of veteran legions — with a sprinkling of old centurions at the head of their number. It would have needed a season to get the new legion into order.

Four weeks was all they were allowed. At that time Caesar appeared, and they paraded awkwardly while he addressed them as "Men of my Twelfth Legion." They cheered him with enthusiasm, less because he made any impression of the sort of man he was than because the words "Twelfth Legion" already meant something. Four weeks in the life of a recruit is a long time. The legion's eagle in the center of the camp had already taken the place which had been occupied in their homes by the spirits of the household. The eagle was the symbol of their common life, their link with destiny. Each man's position as a small cog with a definite part was assured by its presence.

They cheered Caesar, then; and they shouted even more wildly when they learned he was come to lead them into Gaul. Routine was just becoming familiar, and they welcomed a break. The grumbling and cursing of their centurions over the sloppy way in which they struck camp, the awful warnings, damped their ardor not in the least.

That march, however, was another thing again. Of all the marching Varus ever did in twenty-five years of war, that particular march was the one he best remembered. Caesar put his two new legions to guard his baggage train, with two of his veteran legions in front and one behind. This had the advantage at least that those of the Twelfth who collapsed could be flung on the wagons. Caesar was in a hurry to reach Gaul, and the pace he set was ruthless. Nor did the centurions show the slightest tenderness for those whose feet were inflamed or whose burdens were too heavy. The Twelfth Legion, worthless though it might be, was too good for weaklings. If the carts would pick them up, let them ride. If not, let them lie there and be murdered by the hill tribes for what they carried.

To Varus, even the marching was not so bad as the entrenching at the end of the day when one's exhaustion made every stone a rock, each root an obstacle deliberately run through one's trench by a personal devil. Long before the Eleventh and Twelfth were half done, the dark had fallen. The other legions, by now all tight and shipshape, had managed to kindle their fires with all the available dry brush and were frying their biscuits in olive oil, baking their flat cakes on stones, or stirring their porridge. The Twelfth was lucky if its wheat was even ground, let alone cooked; and it huddled together for warmth through the chilly nights. Even its mules got the worst of the forage and might not have got that, had not Julius Caesar, whom they very seldom saw since he rode with the Tenth, appeared in their lines unexpectedly one evening. After that, the men of the older legions were a little subdued, though they did not explain precisely how they had been disciplined.

It was in the Alpine passes that the Twelfth was blooded. The Alpine tribes, who subsisted by laying tribute on merchants, were outraged at Caesar's bringing an army through their valleys. Most of the fighting had taken place in the van against the Eighth and Tenth, but when Caesar gave the tribes a bloodier repulse than they expected, they changed their tactics. If they were unable to stop his army, at least they might plunder it. Even the weapons of a dead Roman soldier are good, and his cloak is worth something. Very naturally they decided to strike at the legions' mules, which were strung out in a long column to go through the passes. They were mainly protected by the soldiers at each end, but separate cohorts — what was left of six hundred men in each — were marching between them.

The eighth cohort of the Twelfth was winding in part of a semicircle under a steep but grassy slope ablaze with scarlet flowers. The sun was out, and the cohort, which had been rained on the day before and had shivered all night, was cursing the heat. It was ragged, footsore, perspiring, red-eyed, and dirty. It plodded along the track, each man with his eyes on the ground, intent on minimizing every tiny inequality to save effort.

It was a deceptively peaceful spot, had anyone had eyes for it. The meadow itself was steep with outcroppings of rock but no real cover. However, at the head of the valley the meadow ended in a great rocky bump which might almost be called a separate hill joined to the mountain by a neck which was heavily wooded. The path quite evidently twisted around this bump and was further narrowed by a tumbled mass on the opposite side from a recent landslide. Varus came past the landslide without even noticing it was there, when pandemonium suddenly broke loose. There was an earsplitting chorus of yells, and a volley of stones rattled round them, hurled with most unpleasant force. The man next Varus put his hand up to his face with a cry and staggered into him, spitting out blood and teeth. He in turn jammed into his neighbor and, reaching to drag a javelin from its sheath behind his back, found it had stuck. He wrenched at it in a panic. The wooded neck and the rocky hump were swarming with men, large hairy-looking men with tunics of leather and long, heavy spears.

"Follow me, men!" The hated Baculus, yelling in a bull-like voice, flung himself forward. Varus let the javelin go, plucked out his sword, and tried to plunge after. A huge barbarian reared up in his path with a spear about two yards long. In a moment of panic, he knew that he could not get at him with the short sword. He tried to brandish the clumsy shield, grateful for it for the first time since he had put it on. "This way, Twelfth!" shouted the stentorian voice ahead. "Come on!"

A javelin whipped over Varus's shoulder and struck the barbarian in the arm. He lowered his spear with a yell. Varus leaped forward, jabbed at him, and was past. There was blood on his sword. Baculus was surrounded by half a dozen men and fighting for his life. Varus leaped on the nearest and thrust him through from behind. His sword was sharp.

The fight was over in half an hour. The barbarians retreated with a dozen mules they had cut off at the price of a score of dead. The Twelfth Legion was not held to have distinguished itself, and Caesar made a change in his dispositions, setting the Eighth to guard the baggage while the two new legions marched behind the Tenth in the van. In this position they came under his own eye, and he was careful to speak to Sextius Baculus and give him promotion. The Twelfth Legion revived under this kindness and became quite boastful, especially as Caesar did not permit their virtue to be tested any further.

Meanwhile, it was already June. The Helvetian horde had crossed the Jura, poured through the territory of the Sequani, and duly begun to plunder the Aedui, whose lands and villages it ravished to the bare soil. Caesar was met by deputations from this tribe and from the Allobroges, who mainly lived in the Province but who owned villages and farms across the Rhone. The Aedui had been for some years officially allies of the Roman people, whose governor in the Province had been desired to protect them. Caesar therefore demanded supplies for his troops and also cavalry, which the Aeduans sent him under command of a chief named Dumnorix. These matters settled, Caesar marched in pursuit of the Helvetians, who were engaged in crossing the Saône.

From its source at Geneva, the river Rhone flows west as far as Lyons, forming the northern boundary of our province. At Lyons, however, it turns abruptly south and flows to the sea. At the moment when it makes this bend, it is joined by another river flowing into it from the north, which is called the Saône. This is wide and placid, so much so that in some spots one can hardly tell which way the current flows. It is deep, however; and the Helvetians with their three hundred thousand, their draft cattle, their wagons, and all their gear had now been crossing it for very nearly three weeks and were by no means over. One of their cantons called the Tigurini, some sixty-five thousand perhaps, lay on our side of the river. Caesar marched on these with the Eighth, Ninth, and Tenth, caught them encumbered with baggage, and utterly broke

them up. Those who were not captured or killed fled into
the woods. No doubt a few fugitives got somehow over
the Saône and back to their kin. Most must have been
killed by the outraged Gauls, enslaved, or starved to
death. Meanwhile, Caesar concentrated his legions again
and crossed the river, taking precisely twenty-four hours
to accomplish this task.

The Helvetians for the first time were dismayed, not
by their defeat, which they put down to carelessness on
the part of the Tigurini, but by Caesar's speed of movement. They noted that he had now four veteran legions,
some eighteen thousand men, besides two new ones, and
upwards of six thousand cavalry raised from the Province or from the Aedui. They did not imagine that he
could seriously threaten their own fighting force, which
still numbered about seventy-five thousand, even after
the defeat of the Tigurini. Neither the Helvetians nor
indeed any of the Gauls comprehended precisely what
Marius had done for the Roman legions. They thought
of the defeats which the Cimbri and Teutons had inflicted
on the Romans for many years. They thought also of a
Roman army they themselves had surprised a generation
back and forced to surrender. Nevertheless, they perceived that even if Caesar was not strong enough for a
pitched battle, they might be wise to come to terms. It is
not easy to straggle or plunder widely in face of a hostile
army.

Hesitating, therefore, between defiance and concession,
the Helvetians sent to Caesar an aged chieftain called
Divico, who had a generation before commanded the army
which had defeated the Romans. Divico offered to go
where Caesar suggested and settle in peace. If, however,
the Romans preferred to fight, Divico was anxious to tell

them that they would have no more luck than their ancestors. The Helvetians had preserved their ancient valor and would enjoy a chance to prove it.

Caesar was outraged. Good-natured as he in many ways was, it was never possible to take a haughty tone with him. While Divico was speaking, he had listened with hardly a change of countenance, yet somehow or other he managed to appear grim. In reply, he did not mince words. The conduct of the Helvetians had been as inexcusable as their insolence. If, however, they would change their tone, offer hostages, and make reparation, he would consider the terms of a peace.

Divico was trembling with rage before the translation was over. Caesar had been at some pains to describe Helvetian actions in most contemptuous terms. Of course Divico answered that the Helvetian people were accustomed to receive hostages and not give them. All question of an agreement was now over.

The very next day Caesar suffered a cavalry reverse. His mounted forces were nearly all Gauls from the Province or from the Aedui. He did not speak their language, had no commander whom he could trust, and was not used to their ways. For the present he put up with what he could not help and marched after the Helvetians, refraining from battle and merely preventing them from straggling to plunder. For fifteen days he waited for his chance and thought he had found it when the enemy camped at the foot of a hill. Caesar planned to seize this with part of his force so as to attack the enemy from behind as well as in front. Once more his cavalry failed him. He had now put a Roman in charge of his patrols, an older officer whom he did not know himself, but who had a good reputation. This man, either deluded by the

Gauls or panicking, reported that the Helvetians held the hill and that Labienus, who had been sent to take it, had not done so. Again Caesar held his hand. He was at least getting to know the weak points of his army.

It was by now the end of June, and Caesar's supplies were running short. He had floated cargoes of grain up the Saône, but since the Helvetians had been moving steadily west, these were far behind him. Meanwhile, the Aedui had not delivered the stores they had promised. When he reproached them, they talked darkly about influential persons with subversive influence. Caesar presently discovered that they were referring to their commander in his cavalry, Dumnorix. This chief had a Helvetian wife, was deep in conspiracy with them, and had caused the recent cavalry defeat by setting an example of flight. Native politics were getting Caesar into deep waters. Dumnorix's brother was the leading Roman supporter in Gaul and already Caesar's friend. To punish Dumnorix for his act of treachery would be impractical, therefore. Caesar decided to warn him and set spies to watch what he did. Undoubtedly patience was the only way to learn some things, and Caesar waited.

Supplies, however, could not wait. The Aeduan town of Bibracte was only two days' march away. Caesar decided to leave the Helvetians for a time, go thither, and get what he needed. Accordingly, on breaking camp, he turned his army slightly north, not parallel to the Helvetian route, but nearly so, on the way to Bibracte.

The Helvetians, who learned this almost at once through cavalry deserters, had grown in confidence. Twice Caesar had made as though to attack them and had not done so. Their recent small victory had been surprisingly easy. They knew Caesar's cavalry was disaffected and two of

his legions of little use. His eighteen thousand could
hardly be expected to prevail against seventy-five thousand. Meanwhile, however, his presence was a nuisance.
Each Helvetian household had started with three months'
supplies. Three months had now been spent, the greater
part of them at the assembly point or crossing the Jura
with no opportunities for plunder. As long as Caesar hung
on their train, they dared not ravage widely. For all these
reasons, the Helvetians were becoming anxious to engage
the Romans in battle. When they heard Caesar had
broken off pursuit, some said he had done it in panic,
while others pointed out that their chance had come —
for by cutting across his new route, they could force him
to battle and drive him away from his supplies in Bibracte.

Since all agreed on attack, it was merely a matter of
turning their main fighting forces around and letting the
wagons with the women and children and cattle come
after as fast as they could, escorted by the rearguard.
Since the two armies were moving to meet one another
by now, and since their distance apart was not very great,
it was not yet noon when Helvetian skirmishers began to
press on Caesar's outposts.

Caesar perceived what was happening, and without losing a moment he withdrew onto higher ground more favorable to his little army. The hill of Armecy looked
down across a valley through which meandered a stream.
The Helvetians had camped by this water the previous
night and were now returning over gently rolling country
to the northwest. Their wagons, still strung out over
many miles, were taking position on a little knoll as they
came up, where they would form their usual circle. The
rearguard, which had not yet arrived, was marching up
with speed to take part in the battle.

Caesar sent his cavalry to delay the enemy onset, posted his baggage on the top of the hill of Armecy, and set the auxiliaries and the Eleventh and Twelfth to entrenching there. Greatly though he needed their numbers, he did not dare use these troops, except as a last resort behind fortifications. There remained as effectives his eighteen thousand veterans, on whose perfect steadiness his future and the fate of them all entirely depended.

Caesar did not know his troops well, nor they him. He had been with them for little more than six weeks, during which time he had been busy learning. As Pompey had foreseen, the skills of a general are not to be gained over-night. All Caesar's officers consisted of young men fresh from Rome or older people recommended by friends he could not refuse. He did not know their capabilities, and the soldiers did not yet trust them.

Caesar rode out in front of his men, looking unhurried and cheerful, as in crises he always did. Quite deliber-ately he got down from his horse and ordered all officers to do the same. When the common soldiers perceived that he was sending away his own means of quick retreat and that their officers were following his example, they set up a cheer. Then Caesar walked down the ranks and gave his instructions.

Young Varus up on the hill was supposed to be en-trenching with his back turned to the scene of the battle. However, since Sextius Baculus had been promoted to a higher cohort, Varus and his tentmates had learned most of the tricks which lightened their trade. While working with what appeared to be decent speed, they were able to keep the whole battle in view. Below them, Caesar's four legions were drawn up abreast, each legion in three lines, each of these less a line than a section, since it was eight men deep. A legion's frontage was nearly two hundred men, all six feet apart and separated from the next legion by perhaps a dozen yards. In front of them, the ground sloped to the stream and rose again beyond. Along the valley, the Helvetians were massing for the attack, while on their left flank their wagons were beginning to come up and the first of their rearguard was racing over the knoll to take part in the battle. It was one o'clock.

"How many, eh?" said a friend in Varus's ear. "Bet my next turn on watch there's fifty thousand. Think ours can hold 'em?"

Varus had dreadful doubts. The Helvetians had formed a phalanx. Gallic shields are flat and oval instead of being curved, as ours are, to fit the body. This makes it easy for them to interlock, and the Gallic method is to charge in a solid mass, trusting to mere weight to scatter the enemy, who can then be cut down at leisure. They were beginning to advance in this way like a moving wall.

"It's coming to a clash," Varus's tentmate said. "Bet you a flask of wine we break . . . Ever ridden a horse?"

"No," Varus said. His eyes were on the Gauls, whose line was bending and swaying over obstacles — here a rock, there a tree which parted them like hair, only to have them coalesce again and come on with an ever-growing roar.

"Nor me neither," the tentmate said. "Too bad with all these horses in here for a getaway. Only, where'd we get to?"

"Eh, what?" muttered Varus, past paying attention. "Yes, of course."

The armies were about twenty yards apart. The right arms of the Romans in all the front lines flew up. Some two thousand javelins were launched into the air at once to crash on the Gallic phalanx. It swayed, those behind still pressing forward, while those in front reeled from the shock. In many cases two shields, or even three were pinned together. Being constructed in such a way that the shank will bend on impact, a Roman javelin is not to be torn out. Many barbarians, after trying to shake their shields loose, threw them down. At this moment came a second volley of javelins, and above its impact rose the shriek of wounded men. This time the phalanx came completely to a halt some ten yards off, no longer a wall, but a mass of men too closely packed to use their swords. Varus's tentmate brought his hand down onto his shoulder with a bang and shrieked into his ear, "That's showing them! Now charge!"

The legions charged with the short stabbing sword which does not require a great deal of room to swing. Presently the front of the Roman line, all eight men deep, became involved. The phalanx was not breaking, but it swayed backwards. Little pockets were being carved in it. Wounded Romans were crawling out between their countrymen's feet. Wounded Gauls were being trampled. The second Roman line was going into action here and there. The battle ebbed downhill. Over all rose the screaming and yelling, the thud of sword against wood or leather, its clash against metal.

The Gauls did not break; but they gave way sullenly down the hill of Armecy, across the little valley, through the stream, and onto the slope on the opposite side. Here the Romans were attempting to regroup when the Helvetian rearguard, which had by now completely come up, emerged from the shelter of the wagons and flung itself on the Roman rear. The Roman third line faced about in excellent order to attack it.

For a long time the battle seemed in doubt. From the

hill of Armecy it was no longer possible to judge the effect. The sun for one thing was declining into the west and shone in Varus's eyes. For another, the sides were mingled in two separate struggling masses, one moving almost imperceptibly uphill, the other back down into the brook. One might imagine from the movement that the Romans still had the upper hand, yet it was clear that their numbers were being thinned. Except for the Eleventh and Twelfth looking helplessly on, there were no reserves.

Hours passed with agonizing slowness. Eventually the rearguard of the Helvetians was back over the brook, their main army a half mile away on the slope of the hill. Yet still the barbarians fought with their clumsy great weapons, giving ground because they must, but never turning their backs on the Roman line. Romans were falling out literally to take breath, and their two lines on the hill were now so mingled that they seemed one. Yet inexorably they forced their enemies back.

It was the end of June, one of the longest days in the year; but dark was falling when the Eleventh and Twelfth were finally permitted to leave their station and join the fighting round the rearguard and the wagons. By now the main battle had vanished across the low hill out of sight and when the Romans at last broke off action there, neither side was in a condition to resume it. The Helvetians moved sullenly off, now no longer in defiance, but abandoning in despair the field of battle, their rearguard, and their families and wagons.

Not all their wagons had come up. This was less owning to their enormous numbers than to prudence. When the hindmost had learned how the battle was going, they had turned away and so made their escape. The bulk of them, however, were formed into a close circle into which the remains of the rearguard had retreated for a last stand. This was a desperate one. The stockade of wagons served as a rampart whence the men hurled down spears. The women helped them, some fighting, some passing up weapons; while even the children crept under the wagon wheels and jabbed at our men.

Night had fallen. The Romans fought by torchlight and tried to throw fire on the carts. In places they were successful, but the wagons were so many — each a fortress — that it was long before they broke within the ring. Then indeed all dissolved into chaos. Screams of women and children rent the air with bellowing of oxen. Here and there a burning wagon lit up the mass. Around others a swirling fight went on in the dark. Our men slew indiscriminately, hardly recognizing age or sex, and well knowing that women and even children had killed their men. People and oxen lay piled in heaps. At last even massacre died away, and reeking soldiers stood panting and sullenly glared at desolation. Terrified groups of survivors huddled together. A little looting, chiefly of small objects, took place. Most Romans were too exhausted to care. The battle was over.

4

THE GAULS AND THE GERMANS

This is the adventure of Procillus, Caesar's interpreter and the son of Caburus. Procillus was a gallant young man, but his position among us junior officers was awkward. Being a Gaul, he was not quite one of us — and then he knew too much. Great issues were being debated in secret between Caesar and Diviciacus, wise chief of the Aeduan tribe. There was also trouble brewing between Diviciacus and his brother Dumnorix. Though we did not foresee it, the rivalry set up between these two brothers would in the end very nearly cost us Gaul. Nobody confided in young men like us or indicated the moment when a war of defense against the Helvetians was turned into conquest of Gaul. Procillus knew. Of course we put pressure on him and were dismayed at what we learned. We had enlisted for a short and glorious campaign, now happily over. In fact, we were still amateurs at war, impressed by the splendor and the resources of Gaul and frankly frightened of the savage German tribes who had poured over the Rhine and who were also contenders for supremacy in the land.

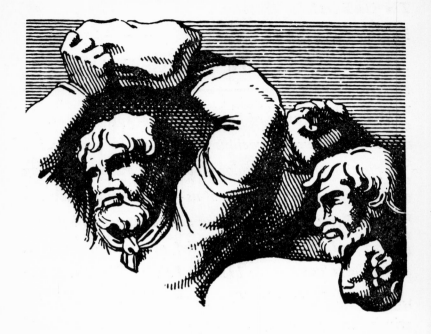

Caesar lay encamped outside Bibracte, the chief town of the Aedui. The slope on which he had settled had once been dotted with the townsfolk's cattle and sheep, grazing between tangled thickets of blackberries which should very soon have been ripe. But by this time the Romans had spaded up the turf for their earthworks, their mules and cavalry had churned the riverbank into mud, and every thornbush, no matter how green, had been rooted up for fuel. In the dusty wasteland thus created between the camp and the river, pandemonium reigned. First had come the traders to set up their booths in rows. Next the local farmers and artisans, storytellers, jugglers, beggars had all flocked out of Bibracte to join in the biggest, loudest, and longest fair the town had seen. The Roman soldiers were glutted with plunder which they had no place to keep save on their persons. Bulkier objects were sold for a tenth of their worth and exchanged for gold or silver which could be hammered into ornaments. Many were bartered for luxuries of a primitive sort. Modest fortunes changed hands in games of chance, were tossed away over a jug of wine and bestowed haphazardly in exchange for a trifle or a timely service. All Bibracte milled around the camp until Caesar was forced to station pickets by the bank of the stream, while the Aeduan magistrates sent their personal retainers armed with staves to keep the crowd in bounds. By these expedients a road was kept clear up to the main gate along which four persons could ride abreast, coming from the ford and the town of Bibracte and the tents of the Gauls in the low-lying land across the stream.

Up this road day after day came the chiefs of the Long-haired Gauls in all their splendor, their bridles jingling with ornaments of bronze and gold. Gold torques were about their necks, gold bracelets on their arms. Their brooches and the hilts of their swords were inlaid with scarlet enamel. They were gorgeous in their plaids and their brilliant dyes, wild-looking with their long mustaches and their hair falling onto their shoulders, sometimes bleached and stiffened with washes of lime. Each had his retinue of raggeder men, each had his minstrel primed with endless lays about his ancestors.

Thus came the chiefs of Long-haired Gaul in their untamed pride to congratulate Caesar. The general constitution of the land at that time was a loose federation of independent tribes, each of which might almost be described as a loose federation of chieftains. A generation or two before, there had been kings. By now the power of the nobles had increased to a point where they dispensed with kings and elected magistrates from themselves, while every chief described himself as a free man.

In a certain sense indeed the chiefs of Gaul were gloriously free. Among their dependents, who were often knit to them by ties of blood or clan, their word was law. Among their equals they were great or small according to their power or that of their allies. Every tribe had its own ambitious nobles who were perpetually forming parties, deep in intrigues with their neighbors, dragging the policies of the tribe now this way, now that way. No undertaking, no alliance of the tribe as a whole could long be relied on. But the chieftains in their pride thought little of that, and nothing at all of the weakness of Gaul, which had imported the Romans to do what they themselves should have done. They came riding to Caesar in Bibracte almost as though he had been their useful servant. They stalked through his camp wearing their long swords, which they drew upon any provocation, looking down from their great height on our stockier men, underlining their contempt by laughter and gestures.

Caesar received them with equal pride. Not all the skill of his artisans could make his temporary quarters other than a crude wooden hut thatched in Gallic fashion. He traveled, however, with considerable baggage of his own and had in addition sent for hangings and furniture from Vienne. The spoils of the Helvetians had included carved drinking horns tipped with gold and other curious objects, barbaric yet rich. Caesar wore his cloak of scarlet and liked to receive newcomers in full armor, wearing a helmet to conceal his loss of hair and add to his stature. In manner he was at his most gracious, yet the loud-mouthed chieftains who came so completely at their ease were apt to fidget and look awkward as the smoothness of his phrases was put into Gallic for them by his interpreters.

Chief among these interpreters was young Procillus. Indeed his importance at this juncture was so immense that though he was naturally a modest and sensible young man, his head seemed turned. There were many in the Province, both traders and chieftains alike, who spoke Latin and Gallic. Caesar used these extensively, both in his audiences and in the exchange of compliments by messenger. But owing to his hurried arrival in the Province and the shortness of his sojourn there, he had not yet discovered whom it was wise to trust with secret matters. Old Caburus was above suspicion. Caesar had met him in Rome and his son likewise. What further solidified Procillus's position at this time was that he through his father was personally known to the most influential man in Gaul and the chief supporter of the Romans, Diviciacus.

Diviciacus was the leading man among the Aedui and in Caesar's opinion the cleverest chief in Gaul. He was a foxy-looking man with dark red hair touched here and there with gray, light eyes set close together, and a powerful body spoiled by too-short legs. He was a Druid, that is to say one of the Gallic order of priests. The Druids were greatly respected, not merely as priests but as magicians and lawgivers. They were the only educated men in Gaul. Their knowledge, moreover, was learned by heart, not from books but from oral instruction, which made it especially hard to obtain. Most Druids were trained in Britain, where Diviciacus himself had studied his art, including — or so it was said — some very powerful curses which could cause a man to die as though by poison.

Whether or not this was true, Procillus did not know. At the moment the arts of Diviciacus were of a different sort, and he was flattered at being made a part of them. Diviciacus in secret session with Caesar had persuaded him that the time had come to call a Council of Gaul.

"Our tribes hold this council every year," Diviciacus explained. "In the absence of urgent business its importance is generally religious. We sacrifice a criminal or two by fire, cut the throat of a red ox, a sheep, and a boar, and perform our secret rites at the new moon. With all such matters Caesar need have nothing to do. It merely suffices that he call such a council here at Bibracte, thus demonstrating that he will be master of Gaul."

Procillus translated, low-voiced. He knew something was being planned far more sweeping than the expulsion of the Helvetian horde. He was closeted with Caesar and Diviciacus alone. Besides, there had been a curious sideways glance from the chief's little eyes as he said the words "master of Gaul." Procillus translated them with a studied lack of expression, not looking at Caesar.

"Friend Diviciacus," Caesar said quietly, "your spells are powerful, I do not doubt. But is it likely that the blood of a red ox, a sheep, and a boar will make me master of Gaul? It takes the blood of men to do that, I think — of fighting men, not your poor criminals. I know very little of your tribes and your council as yet, but it is my impression that the mastery of Gaul is not yours to grant. Nor if it were so would the tribes agree to your conferring it."

"Not for long, perhaps," Diviciacus conceded. "But just now we should agree. We have been delivered from the Helvetians, and we are grateful."

Caesar looked at him coldly. "Not even your own tribe,

the Aedui, are of one mind on this. Your brother Dumnorix, who betrayed my cavalry in battle, keeps open
house in Bibracte. Many chiefs flock to him. I have for-
given Dumnorix for your sake, but you need not imagine that I am ignorant of what he does. You cannot
control him."

Not for all the friendship between his father and Diviciacus did Procillus dare to keep his eyes on the spot of
red which rose in the chief's sallow cheek. There were
secrets to which he would have preferred not to have
been privy. But Diviciacus ignored him. "My brother
Dumnorix is a jolly man in company," he said, speaking
slowly and with evident desire that Caesar understand
him without the use of the translator. "Many chiefs like
him. Many like him also among the Aedui. He has used
popularity to gain great wealth, and this in turn to further
his power. He has always been jealous of me since he
was a boy and I his guardian was one of the chief men of
the state. Dumnorix is no fool. He knows I dare not harm
him or let him be harmed, lest I be accursed for destroying
my own kin. He works to undermine me, fomenting
trouble in the hopes of rising thereby to personal power.
But I have the measure of Dumnorix. Since he plays for
his own hand, he has nothing to offer but a laugh or a
carouse. The chiefs may not like me so well, but I work
for what they all desire. For this reason I lead them."

Caesar put his chin in his hand. "What do they desire?"

"Protection."

"Hm. Well, we shall see. Meanwhile, we will summon
this Council of Gaul."

After this and similar conversations, we military tribunes,
who were the young officers of the army and nearest to
Procillus's age, began to accuse the young man of putting

on airs. To do him justice, his self-importance was due
to the gravity of the secrets he had to conceal rather than
to conceit. It was natural that he should have been quick
to understand what Diviciacus so far had only hinted.
It was even more natural still that he should have felt
awkward with his Roman friends when he knew more
than they did. Unluckily, though, Procillus had a weakness. He was terribly anxious to be accepted by Romans
as one of themselves. He was a citizen with full rights,
yet there was a difference between himself and other
youngsters of his rank. They despised him for being a
Gaul, or so he thought. He was tempted to reveal not
what he had heard, but what he guessed. By so doing, he
might become popular without betraying secrets entrusted to him.

"Mind you," he remarked, "I know nothing special.
But I should not wonder if before this season were over we
found ourselves fighting again."

"Fighting?" someone exclaimed quickly. "There's no
one left to fight in Gaul."

"I knew there was trouble brewing," remarked Strabo,
who was older. "What are we camping here in Bibracte
for? Why not go back to the Province? Gaul's quiet."

"Not another campaign in the wilds!" groaned Statius,
who was only putting in time serving with Caesar because
experience abroad was the done thing for young men of
his age. "I did suppose the worst was over!"

I laughed. Statius by overacting horror at every discomfort or risk had established himself as a buffoon.
"You'll have to put up with it," I told him, not for the
first time. "Caesar's ambitious."

"Yes, but whom do we fight now?" Strabo demanded.
"Procillus knows."

"I don't," Procillus protested, growing red. "I only guess."

"Then you can tell us," Strabo persisted. "You needn't swell with importance and pretend it's all a great secret. Stop putting on airs."

"Well I can guess," Procillus admitted. "Mind you, I only guess that the Council of Gaul is to ask Caesar to drive out the Germans."

"The Germans!" exclaimed Statius in a great squeak of dismay. "Those savages across the Rhine? You can't mean it."

"Not the ones across the Rhine," retorted Procillus impatiently. "The ones in Gaul. King Ariovistus."

"Never heard of him!" Statius shrugged.

"You must have. He sent us envoys in Rome last year and we signed a treaty. He's Friend and Ally of the Roman People."

"Oh, that one." Statius sighed with relief and leaned back against the wall of the hut in whose shade we were all resting. "All's well then. Caesar can't touch him."

"Don't you be too sure of that," I told him. "Look here, Procillus, what is the position in Gaul with regard to these Germans? I don't understand it."

Procillus scratched with his forefinger in the dust, considering. "It's a long story. I'll have to go back to explain it — oh, sixty years perhaps. At that time the Arverni held overlordship in southern Gaul. My cousin Vercingetorix is descended from the Arvernian kings, and glorious they were. But I'll not trouble you with those far distant days."

I nodded with casual interest. We all had watched the Arverni ride in to greet Caesar. We might not have distinguished them from the rest had not Procillus informed us that Vercingetorix was considered the handsomest man in Gaul. He was a very young chief with a high color and a great mane of rippling, red-gold hair. From his profile one might have imagined that there was a trace of Greek in his ancestry, but his complexion and his huge build were purely Gallic. He was gorgeously mounted like all the rest, and he had his minstrels with him. We little thought at this time how many legends Vercingetorix was to give rise to.

"It was the Romans who destroyed the Arverni," Procillus was saying. "When you conquered the Province, you detached a part of their subjects, defeated their armies, and broke their confederacy up. This left the leadership of Gaul to those who could take it, of whom the most powerful were the Aedui here and their northeastern neighbors the Sequani, whose territories stretch to the bank of the Rhine."

"Those same Sequani," Strabo inquired, "who let the Helvetians pass into Gaul?"

"Out of enmity to the Aedui," Procillus agreed. "As you may imagine, a long and bitter warfare ensued between these tribes. At length the Sequani looked for help across the Rhine and invited the Germans, who are far more warlike and savage than Gauls, to come to their assistance. King Ariovistus arrived with fifteen thousand men, defeated the Aedui, and beheld the richness of Gaul. He settled in the lands of the Sequani, and presently more Germans appeared. The Aedui appealed to Rome, but without result. You were content to let the tribes outside the Province squabble as they pleased.

"Eventually the Aedui were so enslaved to the Sequani that none of them dared so much as ask for help, save Diviciacus. He alone fled from his country and made his way to Rome to plead with the Senate."

"I remember his coming," Strabo agreed. "He dined with Cicero and was quite fashionable for a time. But he got nothing from the Senate except a statement that the Aedui were our allies and that the governor of the Province should look after their interests. The governor at that time had no army of any size and could do nothing."

"He has an army now," I pointed out.

"And now," Strabo reminded me, "King Ariovistus is a Friend and Ally too. That treaty was signed last year when Caesar was actually consul. He'll never dare act against it."

"Possibly not unprovoked," Procillus said. "But the Sequani in the end became hard pressed. King Ariovistus had extracted from them the best third of their lands, and it now was obvious that he would demand more in future. Nor are the Germans, who live by brigandage, very comfortable neighbors. It came to the point at last where the Sequani were willing to make common cause with the Aedui and as far as possible with the whole of Gaul.

"This matter came up in the Council of Gaul some few years back. Not all the tribes responded, but a vast Gallic army did take the field against the Germans — too vast an army to provision itself. It was easy for Ariovistus to retreat until they began to disperse and then to inflict a shattering defeat. His terms were harsh, particularly to the Sequani, who were shortly told to cede another third of their lands. In fact, the moment had come which my father's friend Diviciacus had foretold — the moment when either the Germans or the Romans must overrun Gaul. It has long seemed probable that the Germans would be first in the field. Now, however, that Caesar has been victorious, Diviciacus gains his way and summons a Council of Gaul. Of course he intends that a clash with the Germans shall follow."

Statius shook his head with violence. "I don't believe it. No one attacks those wild barbarians unless he must. Besides, Caesar daren't go to war with a Roman Friend and Ally. And why should he?"

"Because Caesar is ambitious to rule Gaul," I told him. "Why call this council else?"

"With the Helvetians," Strabo said darkly, "we were lucky. Germans are quite another thing. Because Caesar has had one success he feels invincible. Yet it isn't as though he's an experienced general. I don't like this."

"Well naturally," Procillus looked embarrassed, "the whole thing's a guess."

Rumors spread fast, and presently the whole army was watching Caesar's negotiations with painful interest. Statius was by no means the only spoiled, wealthy young man who was following the fortunes of Caesar merely for the look of the thing. Strabo and his kind, though older and tougher, were trained in the political game at Rome where a man made his mark by a sharp, critical tongue. They suggested that victory had gone to Caesar's head.

Meanwhile, events were developing much as Procillus had foretold. The Gallic Council had appealed to Caesar in the fine, dramatic fashion beloved of Gauls, all shedding tears. Caesar had sent envoys to King Ariovistus, dwelling on his duty to protect the Aedui. King Ariovistus had been rude. A newly arrived German tribe began to harry the Aedui, and a hundred cantons were rumored to be crossing the Rhine. While our army was still consoling itself with delay, Caesar took one of his sudden decisions. We were ordered to pack up and march. We found ourselves stumbling northeastward through the unknown territory of the Sequani in the general direction of the German horde and of the Rhine. Nor did Caesar give us time to think the matter over. He led us by forced marches to the town of Besançon, which was stocked with provisions and all sorts of military gear. There he halted to wait for his baggage while further supplies were collected from the tribes round about. We none of us doubted that Caesar meant to fight.

Hitherto the morale of our army had not depended on its officers, but on its centurions, hard-bitten professionals raised from the ranks, who knew their men. But the general expectation of ease at Bibracte, the sudden march, the unknown wilderness, and the fearful reputation of the Germans had made even these look grave. In the short Helvetian campaign they had not acquired that blind faith in Caesar which animated us all later on. They had listened to the criticism of Strabo's friends with some respect. Thus when the officers, starting with the youngest, began to panic, the centurions were affected too. Presently all was in uproar.

I had been on a mission to the Lingones about getting grain, and I arrived back to find Statius, who was my tent-mate, packing. He told me he had asked Caesar for leave on account of ill-health. This was no more than I expected from Statius, and I merely wished him luck.

"I'll give you a tip," he said. "Get yours in early."

"Get my what in?" I asked stupidly.

"Keep your voice down, you silly fool," he hissed at me. "Your application for leave."

"But I like the life," I protested. "Look here, what on earth . . . ?"

"Oh, all right then." He seemed to be quivering all

over. "Don't say I didn't do my best for you, that's all.
Though why I should bother my head about such an
oaf . . . Hasn't that boy of mine got the horses ready?"

He fairly flung out of the tent, leaving me quite mys-
tified. I made my way over to Strabo to ask him if he
knew why there was such a hurry.

Strabo told me, "I'm not going to leave. I haven't the
face to ask and be called a coward. But I've made my will.
Where d'you think I'd better send it? Once deep in
these forests, we'll never get away."

"Who says so?" I demanded, considerably taken aback
since I respected Strabo's opinion.

"Everybody," declared Strabo gloomily. "You ask
the centurions. They always know. They say those Germans are all over six feet tall and trained to fight from
babyhood. They say in the winter and in this climate here
they go naked except for a few skins. Man for man we're
just no match for them. You ask the Gauls. They know.
Besides, it's madness to strike up those narrow roads without our transport. We've already outrun our supplies.
That's all very well at Besançon, but it's not safe in the
woods. What we all ought to do is refuse to march with
Caesar."

Strabo stayed in his tent. He said he was not going to
turn his back out of fear, but he saw no reason to put a
good face on things either. Everybody who had any experience knew that we were going to destruction.

I went about the camp myself, and Strabo was right.
Little knots of soldiers were talking gloomily together.
Gauls and traders, who appeared like flies wherever the
army camped, were full of horrible stories about German
fierceness and their human sacrifices and their magic. This
last was so powerful that you could not so much as look

into their eyes. A horrid fascination kept me listening to details which filled my soul with sick dismay. Everyone appeared to be doing likewise.

I ran into Procillus, who had really started these rumors. He seemed angry. "You're deep in Caesar's confidence," I said. "Can't you possibly tell him to retreat while he has the chance. This army won't fight."

Procillus frowned. "I'd never have believed it if I hadn't seen it myself," he declared. "The tribunes of the Twelfth are actually in tears. In tears! You'd think they never heard a trader tell a tall story in their lives! You'd think they'd never seen a German! Why, all those rich young men own German slaves, and have since the defeat of the Cimbri and the Teutons. Italy's flooded with them, and everybody holds them cheap. I never saw one that was seven feet tall myself or that frightened me. The cowardly fools!"

"They're all spoiled rich," I said. The conversation of Procillus was wonderfully bracing. "It's not they who matter, but the centurions and higher commanders. Have you talked to them?"

He shrugged. "Oh, I know what they say . . . the narrow tracks . . . the forest . . . the unknown country. All excuses. As if our Sequanian guides didn't know their own land."

I suppose being a Gaul he felt perfectly easy about entrusting our lives to his countrymen. For my part, from the little I knew of them, I distrusted them already. "If the centurions are disaffected, the army won't march," I said, clinging to that.

"They'll march," he retorted. "Caesar's calling a meeting of officers and centurions. They'll beg to march."

Procillus saw a great deal of Caesar and felt the enthusiasm for him which many such young men did. He seemed to imagine there was nothing Caesar could not do. At the moment I hardly agreed with him. Three hundred and sixty centurions make a rough crowd to convince. Our officers, too, were not all young dilettantes who found campaigning hard. Young Publius Crassus, not yet thirty, had been placed by Caesar in command of the cavalry, and he was training it surprisingly hard. Labienus, Caesar's chief deputy, was an experienced man. Beneath him were many outstanding officers, ranging from commanders of legions all the way down to the better sort of military tribune. Gathered together, all these in their various ways looked very glum.

Caesar wasted no time on how we felt. He was angry; and he gave us a great dressing-down for having opinions on the conduct of a campaign, which was not our business. This kept us silent, for it was true, while at the same time Caesar's contempt was bracing. He proceeded to outline the state of affairs with Ariovistus, and he gave it as his opinion that the Germans would not fight. This naturally made us all look very silly. In detail, and with much sarcasm, he next exploded the reputation of the Germans. Over this argument he took some time, giving us opportunity to feel ashamed of our panic. Then, before we could recover ourselves in any way, he struck. He assumed, he haughtily declared, that his whole record did not allow his competence to be called in question. He had provided supplies, transport, and guides. He therefore intended to break camp forthwith and march. If the army was afraid to follow him, he would go with the Tenth Legion alone. That legion knew him, and he trusted it completely.

There was an immediate hubbub. The Tenth Legion

was afire with pride at the compliment and wanted Caesar
to know that his trust was not misplaced. The other
legions were furious at being outdone by the Tenth and
only anxious to restore their own reputations. In the end,
every legion sent a deputation to Caesar protesting loyalty
and perfect understanding that it was the general's part
to direct operations. These apologies Caesar accepted,
but with a condescension which left the legions distinctly
on their mettle. For my own part, I now agreed with
Procillus that Caesar could do anything. It was remarkable
how we all struck camp next day and marched into the
woods in perfect spirits.

On the seventh day thereafter, in early September, we
approached the German camp, which was near the Rhine.
King Ariovistus suggested a parley with Caesar, which
he had earlier refused. Messages went back and forth. It
was agreed that the two leaders should meet on a knoll in
a plain between their camps, that each of them should
bring a cavalry escort and should mount the knoll with
ten men in attendance. All this was done with much punc-
tiliousness. Caesar, not caring to entrust his life to the
Gallic cavalry, mounted the Tenth and appeared at the
rendezvous with a group of officers, including Procillus,
since Ariovistus, as it was learned, spoke Gallic.

The German people are very much like the Gauls, but
more fair-haired than red. They speak their own language
and dress for the most part simply in skins, though generally their chieftains like those in Long-haired Gaul wear
tunic and trousers. Their horses are by no means equal to
ours or those of the Gauls, for which reason they mix their
cavalry with infantry picked for speed who run holding
onto the horses. This combination is very formidable,
but even their cavalry by itself is usually aggressive. Long

before Caesar and Ariovistus had finished what they
desired to say, the German escort was edging towards the
knoll, while little parties were riding up to our men and
pelting them with stones or weapons. Caesar therefore
abruptly put an end to the conference and regained his
troops, with whom he retreated before the battle could
become general. It did not suit him that the Germans
should put it about that he had treacherously broken a
truce.

Caesar returned to camp with the Tenth, who were in
a state of high indignation, not only at the conduct of the
Germans but at what their officers told them of the words
of Ariovistus, which had been insolent almost beyond bearing. In fact, he had declared that he was well aware how
Caesar's death was desired by influential people in Rome,
and he had suggested that he might find it profitable to
oblige them. This remark very shortly went the rounds
of the whole camp; and the other legions, who were in a
state of desperate devotion to Caesar since Besançon,
joined with the Tenth in eagerness for battle.

Meanwhile, however, Ariovistus continued to play for
time. He sent some more envoys to say that he wished
to resume the conference which had been broken off. If
it did not suit Caesar to come in person, let him send one
of his staff.

Caesar reflected. He had throughout been particularly
anxious to put himself in the right. It had not needed that
remark of Ariovistus's to remind him that the German
had friends at Rome. To subject himself, however, to
more abuse would be undignified, besides being dangerous
in the extreme. One could not trust a savage. Nor was he
willing to expose a member of his staff to perils which he
would not face himself.

"Would you go for me?" he said to Procillus at last. "The king speaks Gallic, and then his present quarrel is not with Gauls, but Romans. Your father's position in the Province will give you prestige, and I will send with you the trader Mettius, who has ties of hospitality with the king."

Procillus very readily undertook his task. He had been feeling guilty ever since the panic at Besançon, and though Caesar had said no word about his indiscretion, he was aware that it probably was known. Being specially anxious to perform this service, therefore, he dressed for the occasion in Gallic clothes, which he very seldom wore, and set out for the German camp.

Messages of one sort and another had been passing back and forth for several days, and on this occasion neither Caesar nor Procillus imagined that the king had any motive but to waste more time. It certainly seems, however, as though he were laying a trap for Caesar or one of his staff, for when he discovered that the envoy was merely a young Gaul, he flew into a passion and shouted that Procillus had come as a spy. When the young man began to defend himself, Ariovistus bade his men silence him with blows and take him away. They did so and chained him like a dog, not only by the wrists and ankles, but by the neck to a tree. It was the boast of the Germans that they had not slept under a roof for fourteen years since their coming into Gaul. By this they meant that they lived in their wagons and in tents of skin which they threw up rapidly wherever they made their encampment. It was in one of these, very dark and noisome indeed, that Procillus was confined under the care of two guards who knew no Gallic. Of Marcus Mettius he could get no word at all from these surly tentmates.

Caesar was aghast at this turn of affairs. He liked young Procillus and greatly respected his father, on whose influence in the Province he relied. It is not the business of a commander to wring his hands over what cannot be helped, nor yet to engage rashly in battle for personal reasons. Caesar was conscious that the loyalty of his legions needed to be confirmed by success. Notwithstanding, he really suffered for lack of news of Procillus, for after the very first, his Gallic spies could not get any.

There followed days of wearisome maneuver, some of which Procillus spent in the noisome tent, and some in a wagon when the Germans were on the move. But on the fourth day, they brought him out, chained as he was, sore, filthy, and half starved to King Ariovistus.

Ariovistus was a huge barbarian with pale hair and beard, more dusty brown than yellow, and colorless blue eyes. He had one hand on his great sword, the other on the shoulder of his son by the elder of his wives. He was watching his prophetess scatter chips on a little fire of birchwood, and apparently he did not see the prisoner dragged forward. Procillus, however, thought that the king did see for all his nonchalance, and that he gloated. It was not possible to look dignified as Procillus now was, but when they ceased jerking the chain about his neck, he tried to stand upright.

The prophetess was a very tall, powerful woman with dirty white robes and a necklace of aurochs' teeth. Her hair hung behind her in a gray-brown tangled mass, and she wore at her girdle a little stone knife. She spread her hands over the flame and drew smoke upward into the air, shouting her incantations to the sky. The king watched her.

A crow flew leisurely out of the woods to the east, making a detour not to pass over the camp, and disappeared across the hill behind it. Her eyes upon it, the prophetess turned towards the king and jabbered loudly. He nodded.

The woman plucked out her little stone knife and came to Procillus, striding over the grass with such a furious purpose that he thought his last hour had come. It turned out, however, she wanted a lock of his hair, which was unluckily cropped short, so that she half sliced it, half tore it from his head while the two guards held him. Very suddenly she slashed at his arm, and when the blood welled forth, she dabbled her fingers and her fistful of hair in that. Then the barbarians let Procillus stand by himself again, and she was gone.

She went back to her fire and started tending it with chips and something which made the flame burn blue. But Ariovistus's pale eyes did not follow her now. They were resting on Procillus, to whom the king said softly in Gallic, "She is divining whether it is better to sacrifice you to our gods by fire today, or wait till tomorrow."

Procillus knew he turned pale. He was a young man of high spirit, but to die by fire on this very day was terribly sudden. With panic in his heart, conscious of swaying as though he were going to faint, he saw the priestess open her bloody hand and let his hair fall into the flame. And out of the corner of his eye, he saw the king smile at his terror. Once more the sense of being gloated over forced the color into his cheeks and made him answer, "No man ever bought the gods' favor by killing an envoy."

"She is divining now," the king said softly again. "In a moment she will know when it is to be." But Procillus set his teeth and would not indulge the king's cruelty any further.

The divination took the longest moment that Procillus
had ever spent. He watched the priestess in silence, trying to make out from her gestures what she was doing.
The king smiled. Presently she seemed to make up her
mind and spoke interminably in German. The king took
his hand from his sword and made a brief gesture to the
guards, who seized on Procillus. The time had come!
But all they did was drag him away to his den, and by no
word or gesture could he get from them any indication of
how many days he had to live.

Meanwhile, daily cavalry battles between the two
camps were going on, but though Caesar offered a
chance of a general engagement, Ariovistus remained inside his camp. From prisoners Caesar discovered the prophetess had told the king he would lose the battle if he fought
before the new moon.

Caesar saw no reason to put the struggle off, and he
imagined that if forced to engage against their will, the
Germans would fight with less heart. Accordingly, he
formed his triple line again and advanced. If the Germans
would not come out to face him, he would seek them in
their camp.

When the Germans perceived Caesar's intention, they
poured out of their encampment and began to form their
battle line. Indeed, the whole camp broke up; for the
women and children with their wagons and carts drove
out to watch and to cheer on their men. Thus encouraged, the Germans locked their shields to form a phalanx and charged the Roman line. Unlike the Helvetians
at the hill of Armecy, they had here the advantage of the
ground, which sloped gently downhill and was treeless.
For this reason they came on at tremendous speed and
crashed into the Romans before the latter could throw

their javelins at all. But the legions by this time were mad to prove to Caesar that he could trust them. Many men of the front rank leaped forward bodily onto the wall of shields, and landing on it stabbed down with their short swords over the top. The rest swayed backwards, but the elasticity of the Roman line was great because each soldier had room. The onrushing phalanx slowed and swayed almost to a halt as the second line of the Romans became engaged with it; and all along the battle the roar of thousands of men in conflict rose.

Caesar was fighting with the right wing and had put his officers up and down the line, for now was the moment for them all to deserve the devotion of his legions. Thus at the crisis of the battle there was no man but Publius Crassus with the cavalry on the wing to observe that in one place the Roman line was in great danger of being rolled over, while in another it was driving the enemy back. Crassus, however, was equal to all, and galloping up the length of the third line, he directed the reserve of each legion to the place where it was needed most and saved the battle.

The enemy turned tail and fled, while Publius Crassus at the head of his cavalry pursued. It was five miles to the bank of the Rhine, and every hillock and hollow on the way was strewn with dead. A few barbarians plunged in and made for the further shore; but the Rhine has a very strong current and is also deep and wide. Few were able after fighting and running so far to struggle across. King Ariovistus came on a boat moored to the bank, but both of his wives and one of his daughters were killed in the pursuit. Another daughter was captured by our men and sold as a slave.

Caesar had mounted and joined the cavalry in pursuit.

The whole countryside was filled with scurrying women and fleeing men, here turning to bay, there dropping exhausted, elsewhere preserving some sort of rough formation which could be dangerous. The Romans swept after, splitting up into little groups, some frankly looking for plunder, others involved in unexpected conflicts. In this way Caesar topped a rise with a small escort behind him to see two gigantic Germans trying to drag along a captive who was shackled hand and foot and made slow progress. In a flash he was after them and, leaving his escort to deal with the guards who had tried at the last moment to bolt, he jumped off his horse to support Procillus.

There were tears in Caesar's eyes as he threw his arm about the young man's shoulders. "Not even victory gives me as much pleasure as this," he said. Nor could we doubt, seeing him then, that he really meant it.

II

THE CONQUEROR

57-54. B.C.

To write in this chapter of the conference at Lucca is to omit in my narrative a year of war. Yet the proportions of my tale, if not the sequence, are preserved. The real significance of Caesar's war on the Belgian tribes was not his conquest of them, which had all to be fought over again in succeeding years. It was the glory he gained, the mastery of his own army, the way in which his power and the threat of his power was felt in Rome. For this he waged war, and for this he came to Lucca and made a fresh deal with Pompey and Crassus, his rivals. I learned many details from Philo, who was Caesar's secretary. I was present, however, at the banquet of the twenty tables, where I heard Caesar tell the tale of the Nervii with such skill as to discomfort both Pompey and Crassus, who had hoped to embarrass him. I was young then and innocent of intrigue, so that it was only at this time that I saw how Pompey and Crassus were jealous of Caesar.

Marcus Crassus, the millionaire, felt out of humor. It had been impossible for Caesar to visit Rome, since by law a proconsul might not return from his province without forfeiting his command. Therefore since Caesar had spent the winter in Illyria, which he also governed, Crassus had gone as far to meet him as Ravenna, the most distant town of Nearer Gaul. It was not that Crassus cared about the journey as such. His health was still remarkable. He traveled, moreover, in a litter; and he took his own provisions and luxuries of every sort, including a tent — though what with his own villas and those of his friends he made very little use of what he carried. All the same, even Caesar's very flattering invitation could not conceal from Crassus that he was going as a lesser man to meet a greater one. Time was when he had patronized Caesar and subsidized him as a useful politician. Now their roles were reversed.

Caesar had received him alone and had been at his most charming. His anterooms, however, were thronged, while all the pomp and trappings of proconsular power had been much in evidence. The streets of Ravenna were

crowded with important people: Caesar's legates and
deputy governors in Nearer Gaul and Illyria, each with
their own train; rich provincials; young staff officers;
financiers; and Senators come all the way from Rome, as
Crassus had. Caesar's own state had been princely, and
Crassus suspected him of a desire to show that the spoils
of Gaul had placed him in a position where he would not
ever again need to borrow money.

"You're looking thinner," he had remarked almost
sourly.

Caesar laughed. "Perhaps, but I am very well. This
life suits me. You know I am always at my best with
too much to do."

Perhaps the most annoying thing of all had been Caesar's high spirits. Crassus, who knew him well, was aware
that success exhilarated him; but he had never seen him
as sanguine as now. There were rumors in Rome about
Caesar's health. It was said, for instance, that he had the
falling sickness. It would have given Crassus some secret pleasure to have believed this, but knowing the malice of Roman gossip and seeing Caesar as he was, he
thought it unlikely. He had contented himself with add-
ing, "And you look older."

With perfect good-humor Caesar agreed. "Why, yes,
I am older. You, my friend, look older too, but you carry
years well."

Crassus grunted. His hair was almost white now and
this caused him secret chagrin, for he was not yet sixty
and did not regard himself as an old man. With his usual
tact, Caesar immediately changed the subject and began
to speak of Publius Crassus.

"Your Publius has a genius for leadership. You should
see my cavalry now that he has taken it in hand. And

you know that while I was finishing off my campaign against the Belgians, I sent Publius south to receive the surrender of the tribes on the Atlantic coast. There are not many of my lieutenants whom I dare trust on separate missions. Galba, for instance, whom I sent to quarter himself among the Alpine tribes with the Twelfth Legion, got himself into trouble. As it turned out, we gave the tribes a lesson, yet had it not been for one of the centurions, a man called Baculus, I might have lost that legion. It is not easy to find a man with the right connections in Rome who also understands war. Your Publius will go far."

Praise of Publius was always gratifying to his father, yet there was a condescension in Caesar's tone which he did not like. "All very well," he grumbled, determined not to be pleased, "but as I understand it, Publius is in trouble this winter among the Veneti on the Brittany coast. I thought you had conquered Gaul. Was there not some celebration in Rome on that account?"

Caesar grinned at him. "Skeptical as always! Some celebration indeed! Fifteen days of celebration, my friend, the longest period anyone ever had decreed in his honor. Moreover, I actually have conquered Gaul. The central part of it has been in my power ever since I drove out Ariovistus. The Belgians, who inhabit the northern part between the Seine and the Rhine, were jealous of this. They gathered their forces and attacked me last summer. I subdued them. These two main districts make up Gaul."

"And the Veneti?"

"Ah, the Veneti and those Atlantic coastal tribes need a lesson. They have submitted to Publius, and they are unwise to rebel or to detain our envoys. But the worst of it is that they hold up my plans for my next conquest. You do not care for the wine, my friend? It is true Falernian, but we have others."

Crassus waved the waiters away. "It is a good wine and well iced." He took a sip. "You were saying, your next conquest?"

Caesar raised himself on his elbow and picked up his cup, which was a rarely beautiful one of Greek design representing one of the labors of Hercules in which he must needs venture out into the Atlantic. Tilting the cup a little to look at Hercules sailing in his magic boat, Caesar said slowly, "What do you think of the conquest of Britain, of my extending our dominion to the edge of the world?"

There was a short silence. Crassus thought it mad, but he remembered how often he had thought this of Caesar's schemes. It was surprising, too, how often Caesar carried them out, and how when he failed he never seemed to lose. Not even Greek traders knew Britain, save by occasional visits when driven off their course by storms. No doubt the country was nearer Gaul, but even Gauls hardly knew its size or shape. If Caesar vanished in the trackless ways of Britain, would he come back? And would Gaul rise behind him? Caesar's ruin would be even less welcome to Crassus than his success.

"You've not the time," he said at last. "There's this campaigning season and the next before your command expires. Besides, before going you will have to deal with the Veneti."

Caesar nodded, his eyes still on his cup. "You cut, as few men would, to the heart of the problem . . . not the fleet, which I am building; not the unknown land, which I have started to explore; but the time. I need an extra five years in my command."

So it was out. This then was the reason why Caesar had been so pressing with an invitation to Ravenna. He wanted another five years. Once more Crassus pondered. If he did not get them, Caesar would be back in Rome two years from now with his army, the conquerors of Gaul. Five more years would put this off, and in the course of them Caesar might be discredited. This frequently happened when people grasped at too much. Besides, in five years — seven from now — Crassus might improve his own position if he were sufficiently clever.

"Would you be willing," Caesar said, "to stand for election to the consulship with Pompey? If the two of you were consuls in 55, we could pass what measures we liked."

"Pompey would want something."

Caesar smiled. "So would you. There is no reason why we should not all have what we want. It is time that both of you were consuls again if you wish to be employed."

This was true. The governorships and the commands which were the avenue to power were given after the consulship, as Caesar's had been. Politicians like Crassus had to weigh very nicely in the balance the advantages of such a command with its inevitable absence from Rome against the advantages of staying at home to manipulate events. With the power of Caesar growing as it had done, Crassus was ready for a change in his own policy. Pompey doubtless was even more ready. Unemployed generals so soon looked out of date.

"I think," Caesar said, "perhaps we should invite Pompey and thrash this matter out."

Pompey's dignity was spared the long trip to Ravenna. Caesar and Crassus compromised on meeting him at

Lucca, which was the town nearest to Rome in Caesar's province. It was, however, a very small place with a few inconsiderable villas and a huddle of poor houses round a tiny market place which had never been intended for the kind of people who were now to promenade there. The news of the meeting of The Three very soon got around. Everybody who wanted a job for himself, for his sons, for his connections by marriage, or who merely thought he might want such a thing in the future, came to Lucca. Two hundred Senators were counted in the town at once. The number of wealthy businessmen was even greater. It was April and the countryside was now well on in spring, which luckily had come early. Tents and pavilions therefore could be pitched, and one or two people created whole villas out of these with patios and flowers and even terraces built overnight and covered with green turf. In all these, private dinners and public audiences went on, though the general place for gossip was and remained the little market. The scramble for notice from one or other of The Three was everybody's concern, yet hundreds of minor arrangements in business, politics, or family affairs could be and were fixed up. The political season, which was coming towards an end at Rome with the heat, was transferred to Lucca and there went merrily on. Meanwhile The Three, though at pains not to appear haughty, had private meetings.

"You must muzzle Cicero," Caesar exclaimed to Pompey. "You persuaded me to consent to his return from exile on condition that he should hold his tongue. Now look what he says!"

Pompey frowned. He did not care for being talked to in this free and equal way by Caesar, and the whole subject of Cicero was still a sore one. Yet jealous though he was of his position, his bond with Caesar was stronger than ever. Julia had not been able to accompany him to Lucca. They were not certain of her condition yet, but they hoped . . . His son and Caesar's grandson might inherit . . .

Caesar thought of the bond, too; and he restrained his annoyance. He respected Pompey's abilities but always had disliked his haughty manner. Caesar's own manner was often imperious now, but he had not noticed. "I wish to be friends with Cicero," he said. "One can but admire him. My offer of a place on my staff is still open. If he does not desire to leave Rome I'll give it his brother. Surely he has other friends whose advancement he cares about. I am at his service."

"I," said Pompey flatly, "will make him hold his tongue without such inducements."

The shadow of an awkwardness fell over them again. It was Caesar who had the jobs to offer, and yet Pompey stood higher in men's estimation. How long would he do so?

"If we hold together," Crassus said, "this question of Cicero will settle itself. Things are not as they were two years ago, thanks to Caesar. Even if Cicero desires no favors, everyone else does so. He will find that he has no support."

"You mistake me," Caesar hastened to say. "I do not fear Cicero. I want to be friends with him for his own sake. He is a person I have always loved and admired."

"If you both would but leave him to me," Pompey said, "I will reconcile him to you."

Caesar smiled at him. "Then you will have my thanks."

This lightened the atmosphere and put Pompey in the position of having had the last word. "We are wasting our time," he said firmly. "We have come here to make a bargain and should each state what we require. Let Caesar speak first."

Caesar was not at all loath. "As you know," he began, "I have conquered Gaul. It is my intention next to conquer Britain. My reasons? Gaul will not be quiet as long as Britain is not given some taste of our power. Britain is a refuge for our enemies now and a source of reinforcement for every little rebel. If I go over, as go I must, why should I not conquer? It appeals, I must confess, to my imagination to penetrate to the end of the world. With the intention, therefore, of conquering Britain, I sent Publius Crassus to winter on the coast near where I must start. He has been collecting what information he can from traders. There is a chief called Commius whom I have made a king." He smiled. It certainly pleased him to let Pompey know that he, too, had made kings. "Commius has influence with those Gauls who have settled in recent times in Britain. He has visited them, and he has told me much of what he can gather about the remoter parts of that great island. Meanwhile, Publius Crassus was to have set sail in the spring when the weather grew better for its southwestern coast where the tin mines are. There the chieftains are accustomed to trade, so that they will receive strangers and tell them what they can. If all goes well, by this time Publius should have started.

"While this was in preparation, the Veneti revolted. The trade goods from Britain, which are chiefly tin, hides, and grain, are carried by the Veneti almost entirely. Hearing of our inquiries and our project, they feared lest their livelihood be interfered with. They therefore formed a conspiracy with the other tribes of the Atlantic seaboard, sent I believe to Britain for help, and detained our envoys. Thus, before it is possible for me to leave for Britain, I must conquer the Veneti. In order to do so I shall need a fleet, for this is a maritime people. Decimus Brutus is building me one in the mouth of the Loire which will also be useful for Britain.

"I should perhaps tell you, for I need conceal nothing from you, that it is not unlikely that other tribes will shortly revolt to join the Veneti. At all events, I must hold them down and overawe them. There is no trusting the Gauls, for such are the factions between the chiefs in their tribes that if the rulers surrender, settle down, give hostages, it naturally follows that the party which is against them seeks rebellion. Thus the Veneti, though hardly powerful in themselves, are causing trouble which may put off my great invasion of Britain.

"As matters stand, I have but two more summers in which to accomplish so much. It is not sufficient for Britain and scarcely so even for Gaul. I would not want to leave trouble there for my successor; and after all my conquest is but recent."

Pompey nodded judicially. "Yes. Well then, what do you want?"

"I want," said Caesar deliberately, "five extra years in Gaul. I want also the right to ten legions. As you know, I now have eight; but four of these were raised on my authority and after war started. I want the right to ten with the back pay of my present four assumed by the state."

"I have always said," Crassus remarked, "that no man could really call himself rich who could not support an army at his own cost."

Caesar shrugged. "I do not ask for riches, but authority from the state. These legions must be paid for."

"I think," Pompey said distinctly, "you ask a good deal."

Caesar turned on him. "Very well then. But what do you ask?"

"Let Crassus speak next," Pompey said. It did not suit him to put his cards on the table until he saw those against him. Caesar and Crassus might have cooked up something awkward in Ravenna.

Crassus studied both of them, his hard, lined face intent. "What I have to demand of you," he said, "may surprise you both. I have not told Caesar. As you know, ever since Pompey came back from the East, the Parthian kingdom has been raiding us across the Euphrates. There has been, in fact, an undeclared war. I want an army and leave to conquer the Parthians."

Both of his colleagues looked at him with astonished dismay. Pompey, who had no particular motive for concealing his thoughts, said bluntly, "You don't know the Parthians as I do. Besides, you're too old. Better stick to finance."

Crassus's little eyes looked venomous. "I'm no fool, and I've conducted a campaign."

"Some twenty-five years ago," Pompey agreed.

"When I see," Crassus remarked, "what stupid people can become great generals, I think there's nothing in it."

Pompey's broad face went scarlet with anger, but he was wise enough not to try the cap on for size, and he said nothing.

"I shall miss you, my old friend," Caesar said with genuine sadness. He felt as though he had reached the end of an era. For a long time he and Crassus had been the brains and the money counterbalancing Pompey. Quite suddenly he had become a famous general with an army of his own. Crassus had perceived himself no longer one of a pair but the last of three. Now he, too, must have his army. Partnership was over.

"I shall need my son when that time comes," Crassus said. "Even Pompey can hardly call Publius too old."

"I shall send him," Caesar promised, "like a prince with a thousand Gallic horsemen." One could not precisely be fond of old Crassus, and yet the moment was poignant. "I would have made Publius Emperor of Britain," he said half smiling.

"What," said Crassus in his cold business voice, "does Pompey want?"

Pompey did not answer at once. He had been thinking. The demands of Caesar had been what he supposed, but Crassus had surprised him. He did not personally want the Parthian command. For one thing, Parthia with its great arid stretches was not easy to campaign in. Pompey had looked at it years ago in his full tide of success and refrained. For another, it was very far away. Here at Lucca they were both in Caesar's province and a few days' march from Rome. What would it profit Pompey to conquer Parthia while Caesar sat in Gaul? Nor could further successes in the East very greatly increase his prestige. He had but to show himself in Asia tomorrow, and all the world would flock to him. Nothing ever could raise his reputation there. He might even lower it by going again.

Then if Caesar had Gaul and Crassus Parthia, what would Pompey do? He could not by wishing make a suitable war. He did not even desire to turn his back on Rome with Caesar so near. If he stayed in Rome — he alone of The Three — his enormous influence might well be increased. There was many a province not dominated by Caesar or Crassus. Most of their governors were friends of Pompey.

All these ideas flashed through his mind. Pompey's slow manner served to conceal his power of careful thought. He had by no means come to this conference without making up his mind, and after consideration he saw no reason in Crassus's proposal to change it.

"I want," he said, "Spain. That is, I want the governorship of both the provinces of Spain."

He paused and looked at the other two. Both nodded. "I want also," he said, "the right to administer them from Rome, to appoint all the people and to be in fact governor without going to Spain."

Crassus looked doubtful. He saw the advantages of this to Pompey in patronage and power, and he saw also the danger of leaving an enemy in Rome. "It's without precedent."

"I've broken precedent before," Pompey said. "Will you take it or leave it?"

"Oh, we'll take it," Caesar agreed. "It's very clever."

The dinner given by Pompey to celebrate this agreement became famous, even among Romans who spent a fortune on dinners. It hardly suited The Three to make public their intentions, but they undoubtedly wished to parade their close alliance. Everybody who had any pretensions to influence was accommodated at the twenty tables Pompey had disposed in a circular arbor surrounding a pool whose wide grassy border gave space for acrobats, musicians, dancers, or mock combats. Every luxury obtainable was offered — iced wine, scented water for the hands, rose petals forced out of season, rare delicacies from abroad. Fantastic dishes were paraded, imitating birds, beasts, and even whole scenes in which the human figures were living children, combined with creations of the confectioner's art, each so disposed and colored that the eye could scarcely tell the difference. It seemed the object of Pompey to give his guests so much to marvel at that conversation on other topics would be stilled.

In all this Pompey showed some tact. The agreement of The Three had not diminished their mutual jealousies or those of their partisans. It was far easier to admire than to converse. If the whole evening could have passed in empty compliments, it would have been accounted a success. There was, however, a maliciousness in Crassus which impelled him to pin pricks. Pompey's poses annoyed him. Thus in a quiet moment between one performance and the next, he called upon Caesar to tell the company about his victory over the Nervii last summer.

There was a silence. Pompey looked displeased at the interruption. Indeed, it could hardly suit him that Caesar should boast of his achievements. Caesar for his part laughed. "Who but Crassus would call on me to confess my shortcomings before the hero of a hundred fights? I will admit my carelessness very nearly lost that battle, and perhaps I may be excused from saying more."

"As the tale was told to me, you did not lose but saved the day," Crassus retorted. "Of faulty generalship my informant did not speak. Yet if the subject is a sore one, you must forgive my lack of tact."

As usual Pompey had taken a moment to make up his mind, but either his duty as a host or his hope of embarrassing Caesar caused him to press the matter. "We hear so many tales at Rome," he pointed out, "that it is hard for us to distinguish truth from gossip. That Caesar has conquered gloriously we know, but under what conditions and with what effect we scarcely can tell. An opportunity to learn the whole story is rare, nor can I imagine that Caesar has any cause to blush for his triumph."

Caesar, to the annoyance of Pompey's friends, seemed not disconcerted. "I know your skill will condemn me for a fault you never would have committed, but I shall not blush. I cannot aspire to vie with Pompey the Great.

"You know perhaps that the northern tribes of Gaul, dwelling between the Seine and the Rhine, distinguish themselves from the Gauls proper and call themselves the Belgians. They are in fact the same race, speak the Gallic language, with differences of dialect, and follow the same customs. The Belgians, however, are mingled with the Germans, partly by intermarriage and traffic over the Rhine, partly by small tribes of Germans who have settled among them, but most of all by their constant state of border warfare. Thus the Belgians are more practiced fighters than the Gauls, more fiercely independent, and more savage. It was the Belgians who resented the presence of our army in winter quarters at Besançon, resented my calling Councils of Gaul and my assumption of authority among the chiefs of the tribes. They seemed, in fact, to imagine that after driving two invaders from Gaul I should withdraw to the Province and, as it were, shut my door, leaving Gaul for the next marauder.

"Such being the attitude of the Belgians, they spent most of the winter forming a league, and last spring they raised an army to drive me back to the Province. Like most Gallic armies, this was enormous. The smoke of its campfires actually covered eight miles. It was also undisciplined, torn with jealousies, too big to live off the country, and ready to scatter in confusion at the first slight reverse. At the expense of little fighting I broke it up and found myself advancing on the Belgian tribes one by one. These readily surrendered, some displaying a token resistance, others only anxious to make terms as fast as they could. You must remember that this was my only campaign against the Gauls, whose warlike reputation was beginning to seem exaggerated. They had not been able to face the Helvetians or the Germans by themselves; and now having challenged our power, they could not face it either. Small wonder our army held them in contempt."

"You had Gallic cavalry, though," Crassus remarked. "And it fought well I believe."

"Thanks to Publius." Caesar smiled at him. "You should have seen how badly it did under its own chiefs. It was true that, disciplined, the Gaul could fight—but in his own savage state we thought little of him.

"Thus confident, we approached the Nervii, who are among the most primitive and warlike tribes in Gaul. They forbid the importation of wine or any article of luxury and despise the other Belgians as degenerate and soft. They had now sent their women and old men into inaccessible swamps for protection, while their warriors had taken oath that they would never submit to us. Gallic oaths are often made and often broken, for the race is impulsive. We expected another easy triumph over this people.

"In this mood we approached the river Sambre, marching in close order as far as we could, but much obstructed by the hedges which are traditional in the Nervian country to protect the people from cavalry raids by their neighbors. These hedges are not only initially thick, but are frequently worked on with a billhook, so that they are horizontally interwoven with partially severed sap-

lings or branches, some still growing, and others further
reinforced by brush or brambles. In this way they present a formidable obstacle, hard to surmount or to see
through. We hacked our way; but time was consumed,
and the baggage straggled somewhat under protection of
my newest and least experienced legions, which formed
the rearguard.

"All this, though tiresome, mattered little. We did arrive at the spot our engineers had chosen for our campsite
on the side of a slope which ran down to the Sambre.
There were hedges running up the hill, but I could get
a clear view of the river and a ridge rising almost as
steeply on the other side. This was thickly wooded, save
for some seventy yards at the bottom. It evidently hid
an enemy force, whose cavalry outposts could be seen
on the open ground above the bank.

"It was always my policy throughout the Belgian
campaign to be aggressive. It saved lives in the end. Accordingly, as soon as our cavalry had properly come up
I ordered it to charge the enemy across the Sambre, which
was here about three feet deep. I imagined, as proved to
be the case, that our better discipline would more than
make up for the disadvantage of the ground. I even was
hopeful that a cavalry defeat would cause the enemy completely to lose heart. This had happened before.

"My cavalry formed up and charged. There could of
course be no question of an infantry attack on that wood
until the cavalry had probed the position and taken prisoners who might inform us of the enemy's dispositions.
Our purpose for that day was to encamp. Accordingly, I
dismissed the legions to their usual task of entrench-
ment."

"Leaving, I suppose, one legion on guard," Pompey said.

Caesar smiled. "You probe my weaknesses at once. But I shall not blush. No, I did not. I was too sanguine for the reasons I have outlined. I thought the Nervii would have small stomach for a fight. I was not certain how far they were even gathered in strength. Our own arrival had been delayed, and then I supposed that the baggage and the legions on guard with it would arrive almost at once. My people scattered into their working parties, digging ditches, felling what trees they could find, chopping stakes for the palisade. Beyond the river, the cavalry engagement was proceeding as I expected. Our men had scrambled up the bank, and had driven their enemies as far back as the trees, which prudence forbade them to enter. Presently the Nervii, having re-formed inside the wood, charged again and were countered briskly. Once more they retreated.

"Suddenly the Nervian infantry swarmed out of the wood in enormous numbers, charged our cavalry, and put it instantly to flight. Immediately they raced across the open space to the river with the obvious intention of crossing the Sambre and falling on my legions before they could form line of battle. I saw what was happening almost at once; that is, as soon as I could believe my eyes. The river was wide and after all reasonably deep. The slope on our side was steep. They had, as I said, to charge our cavalry and cross the open space on their own side. To run such an obstacle race in full armor and to be in any condition to fight when one arrives is a very great feat.

"I suppose I had less than ten minutes to form line of

battle. At the moment it seemed a shorter time still, but I have since concluded that it must have been as long. I sent someone flying to hoist the red battle flag over my tent, which was marked out but not yet pitched. I ordered the trumpeters to sound the alarm. Without waiting for my horse, my helmet, or my shield, I rushed down hastily to where the Tenth was forming on the left, ran down the ranks giving essential instructions, yelled to the soldiers to keep cool, and hurried to the Ninth.

"Here battle was already joined. Soldiers were still running up from where they had piled their weapons, were snatching the covers off their shields, cramming on their helmets, and attaching themselves to the nearest unit they could find. To tell the truth, this battle was decided by months of painstaking drill which Labienus had carried out at Besançon during the winter while I came back here to Nearer Gaul and held the assizes. I did what I could, but the real credit belongs to Labienus, to the centurions, and to the men themselves. It is not mine.

"On the left, the working parties of the Ninth and Tenth had not been far from the scene of battle. They had therefore been able to form a decent line and discharge their javelins. With this advantage, they routed the enemy opposite them and pursued them through the water and back towards their camp on the far side. Next them the Eleventh and Eighth had a harder time, yet they also threw the enemy back and fought them down to the water.

"This left the Twelfth and Seventh on the right. It left also their flank completely exposed, so that the enemy swarmed up and around them through the gap made by the advance of our center. Vast numbers of Nervii, directed by their general, who was quick to seize his chance, surrounded these legions. Still more began to make for our half-finished camp higher up. There they came on the cavalry whom they themselves had routed on the other side of the river. These were retreating up the hill from the far left, having skirted the battle to reach a position of safety. At the moment when they came in sight of the camp, the Nervii charged them from thence and sent them flying down the hill together with a crowd of camp followers who had ventured out too rashly behind the victorious Ninth and Tenth in search of plunder.

"All was in dreadful chaos. The men of the baggage train, who had by now come up, fled in every direction. At this moment appeared a body of horse which a tribe called the Treveri had sent to join our army. Coming on the camp and seeing all this confusion, these Treveri turned around and went home, reporting to their people that the Romans were utterly defeated.

"In the meanwhile, I ran for the Twelfth. I found it in very bad case. It had not been able to deploy, so that its standards were huddled in one place, and the soldiers trying to rally around them were cramped for lack of room. All six centurions of the fourth cohort were already killed. The standard-bearer of the legion had been cut down, the Eagle lost. Sextius Baculus, the first centurion, who had fought like a lion and was covered with blood from many wounds, lay propped against a rock, still calling to his comrades to come on. Some, however, were falling to the rear and getting out of range.

"There was not a moment to be lost. I had no reserves. I snatched a shield from the nearest soldier and rushed into the front line, calling to the centurions by name and directing the standard-bearers of the cohorts to move apart. I had no attention to spare for the enemy and must suppose that the devotion of the best men of the Twelfth saved my life. At all events, my arrival did turn the scale. The Twelfth rallied and began to spread out. I was able to spare some attention for the Seventh, which was in similar case. I edged the two legions together and formed them back to back, after which the fight began to seem more even.

"By this time my new legions behind the baggage train had finally managed to reach the top of the hill. Furthermore Labienus, who with the Ninth and Tenth had taken the enemies' camp across the river, now beheld from where he was what was going on. Without losing a moment, he sent the Tenth back to take the enemy from behind.

"Once again all was transformed. The Nervii, split into parties, were caught between the fresh legions above, the Seventh and Twelfth on the field with me, and the Tenth below them. The cavalry, too, had recovered their nerve and were anxious to erase the shame of their flight. Even the camp followers found themselves weapons from somewhere and made a charge.

"The Nervii were outmatched, but they had no thought of flight. Usually once the chiefs and better sort are overcome, the rest of a Gallic army is rabble. This time it was not so. Men leaped on the bodies of their dead to carry on fighting. When they in their turn dropped, those behind used piles of corpses as a rampart. When ammunition failed them, they caught at our javelins in the air and tried to return them. They won our admiration, but perished where they stood.

"So great was the slaughter in this battle that when the

women and children and the old men of the Nervii received their survivors, they sued for peace. The council of their nobles, so they said, was reduced from six hundred to three, and of their sixty thousand fighting men, scarce five hundred survived. They exaggerated, as all Gauls do, yet in truth the strength of their people was utterly gone. I made provision that the neighboring tribes should in no way molest them. They had deserved it."

"Then you pacified the other tribes?" Crassus said.

Caesar nodded. "With little trouble. One town surrendered and then attempted a treacherous attack. I sold those people as slaves, some fifty-three thousand."

There was a silence. "A pretty profit for you," Crassus remarked sourly.

Caesar shrugged. No real Roman is sentimental about war.

"Profit more justly earned by your legions." Pompey was struggling with outrage. He perceived that by making little of his energy and courage and by admitting his mistake, Caesar had won his audience over. It galled him that a man could actually boast of his bad generalship. "It is surely the duty of a commander to look after his army. Yet in this case, it rather appears that the army looked after you."

"To my mind the first duty of a commander," Caesar retorted blandly, "is to train his legions to such a point that they are invincible. This I may claim to have done."

"I shall look to you to instruct me in your methods," snapped Pompey, annoyed. Till now he had almost forgotten how hard it was to get the better of Caesar in argument, and how much he disliked him.

2

FIRST LANDING IN BRITAIN 55 B.C.

Volusenus and Commius are my heroes for this year, not only on account of what they did, but because the feud between them ran right through the rest of the war as a personal quarrel. They were both of them new to prominence. Volusenus was regarded as a newcomer by our clique and not much favored because his abilities had brought him to notice early. Commius, of course, was king of those parts about Boulogne where our army lay encamped; and he had connections in Britain, which made Caesar seek his advice. His personality one liked or disliked strongly, somewhat depending on how well one understood Gallic. Commius had very great personal charm, but his volubility was an essential part of this. Rob the gestures and the smile of the words which they accompanied, and Commius seemed a comic little man, too easily satisfied with his own importance. He was in fact more than this, as his later history will show. After Diviciacus, he was certainly the cleverest chief in Gaul.

Caesar's power swelled like the Tiber in flood. He and his army knew each other by now and thought all things possible. It had taken a summer of hard, frustrating work to conquer the Veneti. These sea people had strongholds on rocky promontories jutting out into the sea and nearly, or sometimes entirely cut off by high tide. When after much labor the Romans had created dikes to hold back the ocean and piled up siegeworks against the walls, the people merely took boat to somewhere else. They left to the Romans a bare, grassy hillock, stone huts, and a circle of wall which they were at liberty to pull down if they pleased. The Veneti with their children,

their goats, and the very gulls which devoured their gar-
bage were already established again a few miles off. Since
they lived by fishing and by trade, they did not fear starvation.

It had been impossible to conquer the Veneti except
by sea. Caesar assembled boatbuilders from the Province
inside the mouth of the Loire. But his ships when constructed were manned by his fighting men. It was little
Varus who blistered his horny hands in learning to row.
It was the centurions who learned new words of command, the military tribunes who studied the difficulties
of the stormy Atlantic. Caesar's boatbuilders knew only
the Mediterranean with its calmer waters and virtual
absence of tides. For Atlantic conditions their materials
and their designs were bad.

All these troubles the army surmounted; and it was
strong enough meanwhile to send one detachment south
under Publius Crassus to conquer the tribes on the Spanish border while Sabinus went north to the Cotentin
Peninsula and conquered that, too. The army was drunk
with victory and power, ambitious of performing miracles, greedy of booty, and above all it was young. For
the brilliance of its success was draining Italy of ambitious young men of every rank with their way to make,
their fortunes to get, and their thirst for glory to slake in
oceans of blood.

Such a one was Gaius Volusenus, who had come out to
Caesar with the rank of military tribune — an unsatis-
factory start. These junior officers were the amateurs of
the army. Generally speaking, Caesar's political friends to
whom he offered the posts of higher command had some
experience to justify their military ambitions. The military tribunes had none and were not often concerned

with advancement. Their future was in political life at Rome. Perhaps a few of them who had liked soldiering might look forward in later life to commanding a legion in some other general's army. Meanwhile, most were wealthy, all undisciplined. The tedium of winter quarters tried them high, and turnover was rapid. Caesar used them to transmit orders, command small detachments, handle detail. But he did not trust them except in rare cases when they showed special merit.

Gaius Volusenus was one of the rare ones. He was not, for one thing, of aristocratic birth. His future chances must depend on his own efforts, not on his connections. He really intended to rise through military service, as Marius had done, who was Caesar's own uncle and creator of the new Roman army. Tall, swarthy, and supercilious in manner, Volusenus was more forcible than popular, yet he made himself envied by his colleagues because he was never at a loss and got results.

Volusenus had gone to sea with the rest and hated it all. He had quickly discovered that there was little credit to be got out of those cranky ships. Notwithstanding, he had shown himself efficient and had taken part in the sea fight which had put an end to the power of the Veneti. This naval battle had taken place in a dead calm and had been won by the Romans because their ships had oars and could maneuver. There had been hard fighting, yet little glory. Volusenus found himself in winter quarters without the opportunity which he steadfastly had sought of attracting the notice of Caesar.

Here he had better fortune. Caesar's deputy, Labienus, was just such a man as Volusenus, though older. Labienus was stern, ambitious, even cruel, but one to whom the soldier's trade came naturally. He posted Volusenus with a detachment of cavalry, and things went well.

The cavalry of the Roman army was almost all Gallic, either from the Province or from the Aedui and allied tribes. It did not like winter quarters, having business of its own to transact at home, wives to visit, or even estates to keep an eye on. Up to a point Labienus would permit furloughs, but the difficulty was that he actually needed horsemen. There were constant communications with all the tribes around over spring plans, over supplies, over purchase of horses. All such messages were carried as a rule by cavalry detachments under command of men like Volusenus. In fact, it was necessary for the army to have cavalry with it. Labienus made general arrangements to this effect with the chiefs, but trusted his subordinates to oversee them.

It was the efficiency of Volusenus in catching Gallic deserters which brought him at this time to Labienus's attention. Among the chiefs of the Gauls was a man called Commius, whom Caesar had especially noticed both for his abilities and because his native district was the part of Gaul around Boulogne, whence the invasion of Britain would in good time be mounted. Commius was a small man, always abounding in energy and ideas. One generally saw him with his hand on another man's shoulder, earnestly trying with a wealth of Gallic fire to persuade him of something. He was deep in the confidence of important chiefs in every major faction, and his influence was felt in both Britain and Gaul. Caesar had made him king of his tribe. It suited Caesar to make kings where he could because such people depended upon him thereafter. The factions in the other tribes could never be relied on.

Commius was therefore now a king and extremely self-important. He took it upon himself to go to Labienus and complain of what Volusenus had been doing. Labienus was in a quandary. He did not like Commius, whose naïve conceit did not amuse him. He knew, however, that the chief was high in Caesar's favor and that the army would probably move next spring to camp at Boulogne. Volusenus was carrying out orders with perhaps too much zeal, but Labienus was a man of zeal himself and admired this quality in others. Labienus deferred to Commius in removing the young man from his command, but then promoted him to his own personal staff as a sign of approval.

This policy pleased neither party. Commius was forced to be content, but he felt insulted. Volusenus was angry at the change which brought him into competition with young men of smoother manners to his disadvantage.

Thus matters rested through the early part of 55, during which time Caesar was unable to pursue his invasion of Britain. There was fresh trouble in Gaul. This time it was caused by the Germans, two tribes of whom had crossed the Rhine in early spring. The most warlike of German tribes are a people called the Suebi, who had so harassed their neighbors that these latter determined to try their fortunes in Gaul. Immediately envoys from a number of Gallic tribes invited them to join in driving the Romans away and to be rewarded by part of the lands which they freed. So volatile and enthusiastic are Gauls that in their excitement they forgot the tyranny of Ariovistus, of which three years before they had complained in tears.

In a short campaign, Caesar fell like a thunderbolt on the German tribes and destroyed them. Even now, however, he dared not turn his back on Gaul entirely. A large body of German cavalry had escaped across the Rhine, whence they defied him, saying the river set a bound to his ambition. This was in fact the case. Caesar had no appetite for plunging into the trackless woods and swamps of a savage people whose hordes stretched into the unknown north, or east to the mouth of the Danube. All the same, he perceived that while they crossed the Rhine at will and he did not, Gaul would not remain quiet. He determined therefore to make a foray and to strike terror into those people by crossing not in boats, but by a bridge.

No one had ever bridged the Rhine. It is a deep river and also exceedingly swift. In many places it is not possible for a swimmer to make headway against the current, even at the water's edge. Caesar's engineers devised trestles resting on piles which sloped against the stream. These were so designed that the very force of the current held them more firmly together. Over them were laid boards, next poles and wattle work. So practiced were our men at such operations that ten days after the collection of timber was first begun, that bridge was completed. Once more the army had performed the impossible with ease and rejoiced in its power.

Volusenus took his part in these events and perhaps had attracted more notice than he gave himself credit for. Labienus certainly had his eye on him, but Volusenus's ambition was by no means satisfied with the approval of Caesar's lieutenant. What he wanted was his command of cavalry back with its opportunities for personal distinction and adventure. He was restless in Labienus's entourage and rather sulky. But his chance came at Boulogne.

The summer was running out fast by the time that Caesar could spare attention for Britain. His impatience had mounted with the delay. Besides, he had now spoken of the project for two full years and would look ridiculous if he did not act very soon. The eyes of Rome were on his career, as well as those of Gaul. It would be advisable to cross the Channel for a month or so, explore the nearest parts of the island, perhaps win a battle, and conceivably winter there. In any case, he would make his major effort next year with the aid of what he had learned.

Thus reasoning, Caesar encamped at Boulogne and summoned his transports. Despite inquiries from traders of all sorts, and despite the voyage of Publius Crassus the preceding year, he had little knowledge of the inhabitants or geography of the island. On the other hand, as word of his intentions penetrated to Britain, some chiefs sent embassies. Their people were men of Gallic type and Gallic costume, all more concerned with impressing on Caesar the importance of their lord than with truth. However, it seemed clear that opposition was weak and divided. Caesar determined to send over a Gaul who had some influence in Britain.

For this purpose Diviciacus with all his Druid connections would have seemed the suitable man, for Druids are powerful in Britain. Diviciacus, however, died just at this time; I never knew how. Gauls are excitable and spread the wildest rumors. It is impossible for one who does not know them well to sift the truth. At all events, Diviciacus had died. His brother Dumnorix had increased in power thereby, though the chief magistrates of the Aedui for the time were loyal to Caesar. Meanwhile, Diviciacus's place in Caesar's councils was taken by Commius, whom Caesar had made king of the Atrebates.

Commius was delighted to go as Caesar's envoy to Britain. He had a temperament as sanguine as Caesar's own and was a born politician. He now selected an escort of thirty mounted men equipped with all the splendor of brooches and tartans, long swords, decorated shields, and helmets crested with the figure of the wild boar. Caesar gave him a small transport manned by Gallic sailors. In this he departed gaily, having convinced himself that the chiefs of Kent, which is the part of Britain nearest Gaul, would readily submit. Caesar bade him farewell on the shore, while Volusenus spat after him into the ocean.

"I hope the chiefs of Kent turn on you and strip you of all your pretty clothes," he muttered. "I'd not trust news from a lying Gaul. If I wanted to know where and how to land on that coast, I'd go and find out."

He had not troubled to make his voice inaudible, and he drew upon himself a reprimand from Caesar which would have wilted most men, but not Volusenus. He listened quietly, making it clear in a way he had that he would not change his opinion.

Time passed without news of Commius, and Caesar grew impatient. The Kentish chieftains by no means desired the arrival of Caesar and had probably intended to stave him off by sending envoys. For this reason, or else because of the volatility which they have in common with Gauls, they rounded on Commius and his men and threw them into prison.

Caesar was not disposed to wait, for the season was growing short. When news from Commius did not come, he sent for Volusenus.

"I want to know where and how to land on that coast," he said. "Now go and find out."

Volusenus was not in the least taken aback. It was not his way. "I'll need a galley," he remarked. "Much better rely on oars than the wind. No point in being cut off by a crowd of their ships sent out to chase me."

Caesar agreed. "You're not to go ashore," he warned. "This is a scouting expedition, not a foray. If you can't see country for a mile or two inshore, the ground's not suitable."

Volusenus nodded. "An open beach not commanded by cliffs. Flat land inside it, not marshy, not thickly wooded, and not dominated by hills. If we once get ashore, we shall need a safe camp to guard our shipping."

Caesar looked at him, raising his eyebrows a little in a way he had when interested. All he said, however, was merely, "When will you start?"

"The weather's right," Volusenus answered. "How soon will the galley be ready?"

This conversation was recounted to me by Volusenus and very likely lost nothing in the telling. At all events, the galley was forthcoming; and it set out that very evening, hoping to reach the British coast at dawn. Volusenus was gone three days, and the news he brought was interesting. Opposite us, as we could see, were cliffs of chalk. These continued for many miles on either side, sometimes low, sometimes higher. They were broken, it is true, by little bays; but these represented mere folds in the downs, narrow valleys dominated on either side by hills or by high broken ground inland where our Gallic cavalry would be at a disadvantage.

All this Volusenus had seen, having ventured into the mouths of these inlets, trusting to his oarsmen to keep him out of range of a surprise. He had been noticed, of course, and he had glimpsed groups of natives, evidently

gathered to seize him if he landed. None, however, had
come out in their boats to cut him off. Coasting westward
down the Channel, Volusenus had discovered a great, flat
bay broken with islands and marsh and dominated by
wooded uplands. Thinking this no more suitable than
the chalk cliffs, he had turned back again towards the
mouth of the river Thames and had run past the cliffs
once more to see where they ended. He had been rewarded at last by several miles of beach, flat, shingled, and
backed by open country. He had tested the anchorage
here, noted that to seaward there lay a great sandbank
that must be avoided, and had measured the rise and fall
of the tide. He had noticed also something which our
Gallic sailors must have known, namely that a tidal stream
flows down the Channel southwest as the tide ebbs and
then reverses itself to flow back as tide rises. This drift
had great importance for our fleet, yet as I say we had
known nothing of it. Most of our sailors were from the
Province. Those who were natives of these parts gave
information against their will and were not questioned
on matters which nobody had reason to ask them.

We set sail finally near the end of August. Eighty
transports took the legions, while the archers, slingers,
and artillery went on the galleys, which were smaller,
open boats with one bank of oars. Meanwhile, the cavalry was sent to embark eight miles off, where eighteen
transports had been prevented from joining our fleet by
contrary winds. We traveled without our heavy baggage
or much supplies, for Caesar intended to live off the country at first. It was always his practice to put a premium
on speed of movement.

We cast off after dark, about eleven. Caesar raised a
signal lantern in his galley, and we followed by squad-

rons, each of our leaders hoisting a sign. The tide had been ebbing for nearly five hours, so that the drift of the current ran against us almost till dawn. This served us, however, to clear the promontory of our own coast and stand well out to sea before we turned northward. There was a great bustle attendant on our going, creaking of halyards, shouting of orders, groaning of oars in their oarlocks, bumping and banging as our men threw their shields down and tried to settle themselves in their crowded quarters. All the men of the garrison left behind to guard the port were standing along the quays and the shore to see us off. They cheered us, and we cheered back. Those of us who were not too cramped for room peered out into the dark. The moon was sinking, but she was nearly full; and though there was a wispy cloud in front of her, there was still a sheen on the water against which blacker objects stood out. The decks swayed beneath us. We were moving out of the harbor into open water beyond. The little lanterns went ahead; and we followed, wondering whither we were starting to go, how long we would be absent, or who would lay his bones at the edge of the world.

When morning came, we were straggling over the sea. Though the current now ran in our favor, the wind had changed and the sailing transports lagged behind. Caesar anchored under the cliffs of Britain with the galleys, looking up at the enemy forces which could be clearly seen watching us from above. We waited three or four hours while Caesar convened his officers aboard his galley for a council of war. When all were assembled, we moved on at last some seven miles to the open beaches. As we did so, the enemy on the shore moved parallel to us.

The Briton is a good fighter. He wears skins for the

most part, though the chieftains dress like Gauls in woven cloth. He paints his body blue to go into battle, either from some superstition or else to frighten his foes. In this last he often succeeds, for the effect is weird. He fights with spear and shield, and sometimes with the Gallic long sword as well. He carries a knife. British cavalry is poor because their horses are miserably stunted. For this reason possibly, their chiefs prefer to fight from two-horse chariots. Our people were not accustomed to these and found them formidable. They are strongly constructed and move surprisingly fast over difficult ground. There is a driver who takes no part in the fight and a warrior who with much agility will leap forward onto the pole to throw his weapons or jump to the ground and fight on foot. When he does this, the charioteer wheels round and retires to the edge of the battlefield, where he stands ready for a quick retreat or else a pursuit. Thus chariots give the advantages of foot and horse at once, save that the driver is very vulnerable.

Such were the forces which waited our landing, not in great numbers, to be sure, but yet sufficient to cause us serious trouble. The keels of our transports were easily run onto the sloping beach, yet when they touched bottom we were still some yards offshore. Not all of our soldiers could line up one by one on the prow and jump for the shallows. They were burdened with their full armor and shields, while the poops were high. Yet disembarking from the waist of a ship into water up to the armpits, they would be helpless prey to the British, well provided with stones from the edge of the sea. British chariots dashed boldly into the shallows, and pebbles came whizzing about our ears. The men lining the waist of every transport hesitated.

Caesar ordered the galleys to range along the enemy's flanks and attack them with slings and arrows and our spear-shooting catapults, which we had mounted on the poops. This proved effective in clearing the shallows and forcing a withdrawal for the space of some yards. Before the enemy could get up their courage again for a charge, the standard-bearer of the Tenth Legion called out to his mates and flung himself into the water to advance alone against the enemy, bearing the Eagle. All hesitation was immediately over. The men of the Tenth jostled each other to be the first overboard. Pretty soon little parties were gathering round the nearest leader, anyhow, just as they happened to come upon one. They were desperately fighting in and out of the shallows with superior numbers of Britons. Caesar ordered all boats manned and sent them to the rescue of those in difficulties. Presently, we struggled up onto the shingle and were able to form. We charged, but since the cavalry had not yet caught up with our main force, we were not able to pursue the enemy. We let them go and contented ourselves with having won our landing.

Next day the British sent envoys and submitted. It seems the local chiefs had formed no combination, while the more powerful of the British kings inland were not yet frightened that Caesar would penetrate to their dominions. At all events, the local chiefs submitted and sent back Commius and his thirty men, somewhat manhandled, very dirty, and with parts of their equipment missing. Volusenus laughed when he saw them and said something in Latin which Commius, who was far from a fool, understood. The very next night, Volusenus stumbled into our quarters with blood dripping from his arm and said that Commius had tried to have him murdered. Volusenus had enemies enough among the Gauls, and he had broken his assailant's neck so that nothing could be proved. Commius himself had been with Caesar and denied all.

Before this incident could lead to trouble, trouble was on us from an unexpected source. The eighteen transports of cavalry, which had delayed their setting out for some days after ours, at last put to sea. They crossed in the teeth of a rising gale, which by the time they sighted our camp was too severe for them to hold their course. Some hove to. These drifted back to their starting point. Others by running before the wind were swept down-Channel, tried to anchor, but shipped too much water to persist. In storm and darkness they cast off once again and headed for Gaul.

This in itself was bad enough, but this storm had coincided with the full moon. Tides were abnormally high, which our Gallic sailors might have told us to expect, but characteristically had not. Much of our shipping had been beached and was flooded. Many riding at anchor broke loose, were smashed, lost rigging or cordage, and were no longer fit for use.

Our men were in consternation. If they intended to winter where they were, they must have their heavy equipment. Yet how were they to return without their ships? It was early September, and not too long remained before the autumn storms. There were no materials for refitting nearer than Gaul.

Caesar was immediately active to repair damage. Thinking over our expedition in the light of later experience, I perceive that he had been rash. This was the fault to which Caesar was most prone, for his temperament was sanguine and impatient. He had ventured at the end of summer, with few supplies, and scarcely knowing what he would find. However, if he sometimes took great risks, Caesar was also swift to perceive his errors. On this occasion, he used the metal and timbers from the most damaged ships to repair others and set his men to gathering the grain which was ripe all about them in the fields. Meanwhile the natives, who had already sent some hostages, were beginning to make excuses. Caesar suspected they saw a chance to cut off our men from returning to Gaul and hoped to destroy us.

Matters were proceeding in this way when the Seventh were sent out again to harvest the grain. By now we had gathered most of what we could easily reach, and it was simple for the enemy to guess where we would go. Accordingly, as soon as the soldiers had scattered, laid their arms aside, and fallen each to his task, a mass of chariots charged out of the nearby woods and fell upon them. All was in confusion at once. Caesar's Legate in charge had not thought to post an adequate guard. The men of the legion assembled more or less and tried to fight back, all huddled together, some with their arms, some not. The chariot fighters, who were new to them, increased their difficulties.

Luckily the pickets at the camp gate reported to Caesar that a cloud of dust could be seen in the direction that the Seventh Legion had taken. Caesar delayed not an instant. He took the two cohorts who were on guard under arms and marched to the rescue, bidding the rest of his men follow. His arrival was timely. The Britons broke off the battle, and the Seventh Legion recovered its nerve. But with no cavalry, Caesar could make no pursuit. He retreated to camp.

There followed a number of days of rainy weather, which is very common in Britain, and which kept our men in camp. The British, however, were once more openly at war and actively collected a great host of foot and horse soldiers with which they marched upon us.

Caesar drew up his legions and won an easy victory, which he could not, however, take much advantage of, since he had no cavalry but Commius and his thirty. These pressed hard in pursuit and aided us stoutly, but their numbers were far too few to turn retreat into a rout. Our infantry pursued as far as they were able, then marched back to camp.

Caesar had made up his mind to return to Gaul. He could see little profit in remaining near the beach, yet he dared not divide his small army or, without cavalry, advance. He had learned a good deal, and by building more and better ships he would be able to return next year in force. Meanwhile, the equinox was approaching and with it the time of storms. Very luckily, our recent victory had discouraged the enemy again, so that their envoys once more asked for peace. Caesar was therefore able to retire with dignity. He demanded hostages, but would not even stay while they were collected. Let them be delivered in Gaul. Then, cramming his soldiers on board his remaining ships, he hastily departed.

3

This year brought another newcomer, Quintus Cicero, under whom I served for my remaining years in Gaul. He was for the moment little more than an onlooker, being too prominent for junior command and too inexperienced to have charge of a legion. Indeed for this year the chief part belongs to none but Caesar. The invasion of Britain was Caesar's high tide of conquest. Even before he made it, there were signs for the discerning that this was so. The death of Dumnorix and the intrigues of Indutiomarus, the Treveran chief, could be likened to the rumble of a distant thunder in Gaul. The death of Julia was thunder of a more sinister sort because it came from Rome. Our British adventure became the end of something for us and not the beginning. What lay ahead was not another conquest, but the real subjugation of Gaul.

QUINTUS CICERO was a man whom people inevitably thought of merely as a brother of the great Marcus. This was hard on Quintus because he suffered by the comparison. Quintus dabbled in literature, yet not successfully. His conversation was witty, yet one missed his brother's sparkle. What in Marcus Cicero was the excitable temperament of a great artist in words appeared in Quintus as the mere irritability of a man with a nervous stomach who did not get on with his wife. Even in appearance one saw the likeness between the two, yet Quintus was smaller, more pinched in expression. In short, while Marcus possessed both genius and charm, his brother had neither. Inevitably Quintus tried to compensate for his disadvantages by being assertive in manner. He took too sudden dislikes or tried to bully, thus often concealing the abilities he did possess and his good intentions.

Quintus sat in his tent at Boulogne at work on a tragedy in verse, his fourth in two weeks. He had found time
besides to commence a letter to his brother complaining
of too much to do in military life. What he meant was
not precisely that he was busy, though Caesar had in
the most flattering way taken him everywhere. He meant
that the bustle of the great expedition to Britain was ex-
hausting. Quintus Cicero had held minor offices at Rome
and abroad. He was used to administration, if not to soldiering. Nothing had prepared him for the pace at which
Caesar lived. The two had posted together in Caesar's
headlong style from Italian Gaul to the Atlantic coast at
the opening of this campaigning season. There Caesar
had inspected the ships being built, had given orders for
an assembly at Boulogne, had collected four legions.
Taking Cicero with him, he had set off very nearly two
hundred miles to deal with the Treveri.

The Treveri were a Belgian tribe, that very tribe whose
horsemen had arrived at Caesar's camp at the crisis of his
battle with the Nervii. The Treveri had gone home, reporting that Caesar was defeated. By the time this proved
false, the opposition party among their chiefs had the upper hand. They had not precisely rebelled against Caesar,
but neither had they sent him their cavalry back again.
None of them had attended Caesar's annual Council of
Gaul. They were known to have sent embassies to the
Germans asking for help last year, and it was suspected
they had done so again. The leader and fomenter of the
trouble was a chief named Indutiomarus, who had the
reputation of being a crafty man and deep in the coun-
sels of other Belgian chiefs whose loyalty was doubtful.
Inevitably, Indutiomarus had a bitter enemy and rival who

was disposed to be friendly to Caesar. Naturally on Caesar's approach this man fled to his camp and told him all he knew. But Indutiomarus was too clever to be forced into war. He submitted, confident that Caesar did not want to be distracted from his invasion of Britain. His hostages were duly accepted, oaths were sworn, and quarrels patched up. Caesar turned his back on Indutiomarus and marched to Boulogne as quickly as he had come. For his part, the Treveran chief was content to wait for a better chance. Perhaps a disaster to the fleet or a defeat in Britain would offer it to him.

Now Quintus Cicero sat in his tent, tired out with travel and getting used to the hurly-burly caused by Gauls — eight legions, over eight hundred ships of all sizes, sailors, traders, muleteers, officers' servants, and the hundreds of hangers-on which any encampment would collect in the twinkling of an eye. The great invasion of Britain had seized the popular imagination in Rome now that Caesar's crossing last year had proved a conquest possible. Young men were flocking to join. Ambitious men were seeking jobs from Caesar more frantically than ever. Publius Crassus, departing for the East with his thousand horsemen, was thought of as missing, not as going to seek a great adventure. No less than a hundred and fifty of the ships to sail with Caesar had been built by private persons at their own cost. No doubt the bulk of them intended to get back their investment in plunder, yet it was established that Britain had no great wealth — no gold — a little tin — slaves certainly, but these untrained and not of great value. Glamour and glory outweighed all chance of profit.

Glamour was not for Quintus Cicero, who was going to

Britain to further his career. Yet even Quintus as he sat
in his little tent over his pedantic verses was conscious of
the stirring of the moment. Was not Marcus vowing to
write an epic on Britain which his brother's descriptions
were to inspire? Was not Caesar gaily writing to Marcus
that he would make Cicero's friends into kings if he
wanted? Had not the patched-up friendship between
these two great men risen to intimacy on the wings of
their brilliant imaginations? Of the two, Caesar was the
more exalted. The opportunity and the risk were his. He
also had something at stake which Quintus spared no
thought for. After disappointment, after miscarriage,
Julia's time at last was drawing near. The heir to the power
of The Three would be born — if all went well — while
his grandfather was crowning his career by the conquest
of Britain.

Across the camp in the section reserved for Gauls,
Dumnorix the Aeduan sat in his tent likewise. He was not
alone. Three chiefs sat with him, cross-legged on the floor
in Gallic fashion, eating from low tables. There was a
bustle of servants, but the lack of privacy was a customary
thing and did not concern them.

Dumnorix was a handsomer man than Diviciacus, besides being ten years younger than his great brother had
been. He was tall and burly, dressed richly even for a
Gaul, and carried himself with jovial assurance. At the
moment, however, his broad red face was serious. He said,
"I know I am spied on, but I too have my spies. Why do
you imagine that Caesar collects his enemies to sail with
him for Britain, leaving his friends behind? I tell you, he
plans to murder us all when he has us at his mercy in that
trackless wilderness."

"Commius is going," protested one of the chiefs, unconvinced. "He would not agree to our murder. We all know Commius."

Dumnorix spat disgustedly, but he set himself to counter the arts of that master of persuasion, urging the chieftains to take their men home. If all of them did so, Caesar could hardly prevent them. But the chiefs neither agreed nor disagreed. They feared Caesar, and the words of Commius were powerful.

In spite of this present failure, trouble was brewing in that spacious tent of Dumnorix's where the servants, some of whom were in Caesar's pay, picked up what news they could from their chief's conversation. To no people had Caesar's occupation brought more profit than to the Aedui. Delivered from the Germans and the Helvetians on their borders, made pre-eminent in Councils of Gaul, granted overlordship of many lesser tribes, the Aedui had assumed the position for which they had struggled so long. They were the chief tribe in Gaul. The real advantage had gone, of course, to the leaders of Caesar's party — Diviciacus and various senior men whose hopeless struggle with the Germans and the Sequani had reconciled them long ago to the coming of the Romans.

To the party of Dumnorix, the rule of Caesar represented loss of authority within the tribe. Their ambitions had always been wild. There had been a plot at one time to use the Helvetians to make Dumnorix king. This had failed, but a successful rebellion against Caesar would accomplish the same thing, while confirming the Aedui as leaders of free Gaul. In fact, the Aeduan state, though still apparently loyal, was actually rent by intrigue. Diviciacus might have held his people together. His death gave power to Dumnorix, but exposed him to Caesar's

vengeance, which he feared. Fearing, he grew wilder.
Caesar had recently invited him in flattering terms to lead
the cavalry of the Aeduans in Britain. The truth was, of
course, that it would be dangerous to leave him behind.

Dumnorix was determined not to go. He actually did,
or so he said, fear murder. Far more important, his real
chance must depend on Caesar's absence. Dumnorix protested he was afraid of the sea. He was always seasick. He
was unused to sailing. He had religious scruples in the
matter. Caesar blandly was adamant. Eventually Dumnorix tried to persuade the other chiefs whom Caesar had
summoned that their lives depended on refusing to sail.

"Caesar is too powerful to be refused," said the eldest.
"Eight hundred ships! Eight legions! Such an assembly
of fighting men and machines has never been known."

"If you do not dare, I shall desert without you," Dumnorix asserted. "Now that the order for embarkation has
gone out, Caesar will be too busy to prevent me. You shall
see."

"Perhaps we will follow. Let us wait and consider."
The chief who said this was actually planning to report
Dumnorix's words to Caesar.

Caesar acted with his usual decision. If Dumnorix and
his Aeduan cavalry defied him, it might be a signal for
revolt against the three legions which he was to leave behind with Labienus. Caesar dispatched a very large body
of horse to bring back Dumnorix, instructing them to use
force if he resisted. Dumnorix perceived he had gone too
far, and Diviciacus was not here to speak for him with
Caesar now. In desperation he drew his sword and
shouted to his tribesmen to come on, yelling at the top
of his voice that he was a free man and belonged to a free
country. Thus crying loudly on the name of freedom,

Dumnorix died like a chief of the old fashion. As for the Aedui, they returned very meekly to Caesar.

There was whispering about the death of Dumnorix, but little was said aloud, even by the Gauls. Quintus Cicero, who was hardly accustomed to the confusion yet, was actually unaware of what had been done. Caesar's new transports, five hundred and forty in number, had been built both shallower and broader for convenience in unloading on open beaches. They were to be rowed as well as sailed, and the versatile legionaries must again in large numbers be trained to use an oar. Quintus, whose duty it would be to command a legion as soon as he was ready, was studying his task under conditions by no means easy for him. It had, however, taken time to gather the armada, and the winds were not favorable. June had worn away before all was ready — five of the legions, two thousand Gauls and their horses, seamen, slingers and archers, catapults, transport cattle, heavy baggage and supplies. All this weighed anchor on the sixth of July with a southwest wind, the men in every transport raising a cheer as they debouched from the harbor.

All went well. The ships duly grounded about noon of the next day, and we went ashore. As we soon learned from peasants, the extraordinary sight of a fleet of eight hundred ships had terrified the people who had gathered to oppose our landing. They had retreated to entrench themselves on higher ground a little inland.

Caesar called a council of senior officers at once. Quintus Cicero, despite his experiences with Caesar in April and May, was astonished to discover that he intended to attack that very day. The transports might be anchored for lack of time to draw them up the beach. The moon, Caesar noted, was this time new, not full; so that the catastrophe of last year did not appear to threaten. He would leave a guard behind to protect the fleet.

There was reason for this haste. A lightning victory might establish Caesar's hold on Kent. If he intended to conquer southeastern Britain this year, he needed to hurry. After the equinox, he could hardly transport troops and supplies across the Channel. Besides, the decision was in keeping with the spirit of his army. It was afire with ambition, and its confidence in Caesar's genius was almost a religious frenzy. Not even seasickness could damp its ardor.

We marched eleven miles, and in late afternoon came to a river of no particular size on which lies a hamlet called Canterbury. Across the stream lay wooded heights, from which the cavalry and chariots of the British descended to meet us. Their main forces lay in a large earthwork protected by a ditch. Points of access were further blocked by heaps of tree trunks. These defenses were fairly formidable, but the confidence of our legions had risen to such a pitch that nothing could withstand them. They formed a shelter of shields and under its protection filled up the ditch. They stormed the rampart and sent the enemy flying into the woods, where Caesar, considering the lateness of the hour, refused to follow.

Next day fate dealt us a blow. The real defense of Britain is not the fighting qualities of the natives, but the Channel. It is the ocean which cut our campaigning season down to less than two months and which at the moment of success robbed us of its fruits. Caesar was preparing to pursue the foe with every prospect of overwhelming Kent as he had done the Belgians after his defeat of the Nervii. Hardly had he started before an urgent message recalled him to the beach.

Last year the full moon had brought us disaster. This year it was the new moon, whose tides — though we had not known this — are very nearly as bad as the full moon's. On those open beaches when wind and waves arose, there was no protection save the strength of cable or anchor. Neither sufficed. Ships dragged and banged into one another. Ships broke loose and were driven ashore. All the confusion and wreckage of the last year was repeated, but on a larger scale because our fleet was enormous. Forty vessels were actually destroyed, and the refitting of the remainder was a problem.

Now Quintus Cicero could measure the quality of the army and its general after a reverse. Caesar had been careless. In his haste to deal with the enemy before him, he had neglected the enemy behind. He lost no moment in repairing his error. Leaving the Britons to recover morale, he sent to Labienus at Boulogne for all the shipwrights he could spare, and ordered him besides to build more ships. Meanwhile, he set his legions to hauling everything up the beach with improvised capstans and rollers of greased logs. Next, the camp and the ships were enclosed in a line of continuous entrenchments. The men were divided into shifts and worked night and day as though possessed.

By a miracle of energy, in ten days all was completed. Caesar immediately marched out to Canterbury again, but found much larger forces in his way. There was in fact a king called Cassivellaunus, who had large territories north of the Thames. The smaller chiefs of Kent had been by no means inclined to accept his help, from a very natural distrust of his ambitions. After their defeat, however, they were more humble. Cassivellaunus had taken charge of their defense and had collected a very formidable mass of chariots. Our men were not able to cope successfully with

these. To be sure, our infantry unless surprised could not
be broken. But the chariots came on swiftly and knew the
country well, so that they succeeded in catching us from
time to time at a disadvantage. If we repulsed them, they
turned and fled, pursued by our cavalry. When they had
enticed this away from our infantry lines, they leaped to
the ground and easily repulsed it. Caesar needed cavalry
of a different sort. The decisive victory which had seemed
within his grasp two weeks ago appeared to elude him.

Luckily, barbarians are impatient. In a pitched battle
the Britons were no sort of match for the legions, but
their superior numbers and our difficulties gave them confidence. Presumably also Cassivellaunus had the usual
trouble in holding his levies together. They made, at
any rate, an attack on our camp in force. They were utterly defeated and scattered. Cassivellaunus was unable
to muster his infantry again and relied hereafter almost
entirely on irregular tactics with his chariots. Possibly he
did this out of prudence or possibly because he could not
do otherwise. But Cassivellaunus, apart from Vercingetorix, seemed to have more understanding of the art of
war than any barbarian chief. We Romans never saw him
face to face, save in battle; but he was a great king in
Britain in his day, and his son rules there still.

Meanwhile, he had his own troubles. There was a people called the Trinobantes whose lands bordered on his
own and whom he had reduced to subjection in the preceding year. The prince of this people had fled to Boulogne
and appealed to Caesar. With him Commius had, of course,
become intimate. It was Commius's opinion that the two
of them appearing in the country of the Trinobantes at
this time would induce that people to put itself in Caesar's
hands. Nothing daunted by his ill luck last year, Com-

mius set out therefore and was within a short time successful. Caesar meanwhile marched the legions straight for
the Thames and the lands of Cassivellaunus.

We marched for a week. The southern part of Britain
is rolling country with high chalk downs and very fertile
valleys which are green from too much rain. There is a
great deal of marshland because of this heavy rainfall, but
the rivers are gentle and, except for the Thames, of no great
size. The people live much as the Gauls do, save that their
civilization is noticeably more primitive. Yet the country is wealthy, too, and highly populated. There was much
tillage in all the part we saw, though farther inland men
are wilder, as they say, and live by hunting or raiding one
another's cattle.

Cassivellaunus made a stand at our crossing of the
Thames. He had planted the bed of the river with sharpened stakes and lined the far bank with them also. But
he had no catapults or slingers, and our cavalry got through
without too much loss. The legions followed boldly,
though in some cases their heads were hardly above water.
Cassivellaunus gave way again and hung on our flanks as
we marched through his own country. Because of the
number of his chariots, we dared not send our cavalry out.
What devastation we did was done by the legions themselves in their line of march. This came to little, since
British huts are mere wattle and clay, and all the people
had fled with their cattle and their possessions. Wheat
was still standing in the fields; and, where we could, we
gathered that.

We moved through the land north of the Thames at
will, doing little damage. However, the fugitives from
our line of march were forced to gather somewhere. Men
with their cattle had betaken themselves to a great wood,

protected partly by marsh and partly by felled trees. Within its recesses they had also made a stronghold with a ditch and a rampart round the summit of a hill not easy of access. After much trouble we stormed this, taking great booty in cattle and scattering the survivors into the forest.

This victory, however, came too late. No sooner had Caesar crossed the Thames than Cassivellaunus induced the chiefs of Kent to attack our ships. The place had been fortified by a wall and towers, so that they were beaten off. Nevertheless, Caesar was impelled to go back to Kent in person and see to the safety of his communications. When he got there, he found that Labienus had sent him gloomy news of intrigues in Gaul. Trouble certainly was brewing among the Treveri, possibly elsewhere. Three legions could not be expected to do more than protect Boulogne.

With his usual clarity of thinking, Caesar accepted the necessity of turning his back upon Britain. He had certainly hoped to winter there, but by grasping at too much he would lose all. Nothing prevented him, as far as he knew, from coming again. He was aware that expectation had risen to fever pitch in Rome and that disillusion would set in when he returned, but it could not be helped. The shortness of the season had defeated him — that and his fears for Gaul. Luckily Cassivellaunus, oppressed by his own troubles, sent men to Commius to negotiate a submission.

It was just in time, and yet again too late. Caesar was able to depart with his men before the stormy season and to proclaim himself victor. He was not able to enforce a real submission and quarter some legions in Britain. He consoled himself that a beginning had been made. The actual business of conquest had certainly been shown to be easy. Further knowledge of the Channel waters could be exploited. Notwithstanding, Caesar understood that for the first time he had received a setback. Cicero's epic on the conquest of Britain could not yet be written. Caesar did not know, however, that fate was preparing an even greater disappointment. When he landed in Gaul there were letters brought to him from Rome. His daughter Julia had died in giving birth to an infant who lived but two or three days. The growing jealousy between Caesar and Pompey was not to be decently screened any longer. The bond between the rival generals was to become nothing more than a fading sorrow.

III

THE REBELS

54-51 B.C.

1

LOSS OF A LEGION

Rebellion broke on us like a thunderclap that autumn. I was lucky, for Quintus Cicero was the hero of the hour, and I served with him. I might so easily have been with Sabinus and Cotta and died in that wooded valley where a legion was massacred almost to a man. As it was, however, we moved our winter quarters to Amiens, where our evenings with Caesar gave rise to the idea of this book.

THERE WAS vague unrest in Gaul when Caesar returned. He held a council at Amiens to which the chieftains came complaining of drought and a bad harvest. Supplies were not adequate in any one spot for quartering the legions. Caesar determined to let each winter in a different place, all chosen to depend on separate tribes, yet close together. With a single exception, a circle of a hundred miles must cover them all. Still, Caesar was uneasy. His eight independent commanders varied from the experienced Labienus to Quintus Cicero with one short summer behind him. Many tribes were secretly waiting for a chance to revolt. Caesar determined to remain at Amiens a while and watch events. Perhaps when the legions had reached their winter cantonments and fortified them, he might visit Nearer Gaul according to his custom.

His foresight was justified. The legions had hardly

been settled in their quarters for two weeks when rebellion broke out. The signal for trouble was the murder of one of the petty kings whom Caesar had made. No sooner, however, had Caesar despatched the nearest legion to look into this than the Eburones, who live between the Rhine and the Meuse, yielded to the secret entreaties of the Treveran chief Indutiomarus. Falling suddenly on a small detachment sent out by the nearby legion to cut wood, the Eburones overwhelmed it and marched against the camp in great force.

The commander of this legion was Sabinus, who had conquered the Cotentin the year before. He was a heavy man, more obstinate than firm, more highly thought of for application than for intelligence. Caesar had used him on several occasions with fair success and by now had formed the habit of associating with him a younger man, Lucius Cotta, who had done very well with cavalry. Cotta's boldness might counteract some of Sabinus's faults.

On this occasion, Sabinus did what he ought, which was perfectly simple. The legion repulsed the Gallic assault, while its cavalry sallied and gained some advantage. Sabinus's position, however, was awkward. He depended on the Eburones for grain. Most luckily, they had delivered supplies a few days before. He was, however, fifty miles from Cicero, almost as far from Labienus, and besieged by a milling mob of barbarian forces. His camp as yet was but half constructed; and, though fortified, it was not as strong as it ought to be. Should he merely withstand his attackers and hope they would melt away? The Gauls were shouting that they wanted a parley. Sabinus, too, required time for thought and discussion. He sent out to them Arpineius, accompanied by a Spaniard who spoke Gallic and had already been sent on Caesar's errands to the Eburones.

The chief man among the Eburones was Ambiorix, with whom we had all of us had frequent dealings. The Eburones were not in themselves a powerful tribe, and they had earlier been dependents of the Aduatuci. These people had attempted treachery against Caesar after the crushing of the Nervii and had been severely dealt with. The Eburones as a matter of course had profited. Caesar had freed them from the tribute they used to pay the Aduatuci and had ordered the release of their hostages, including the son and nephew of Ambiorix himself. It naturally followed that Ambiorix and his tribe had been a group upon which Caesar had relied.

All this Ambiorix now poured into Arpineius's ear, making excuse to take the Romans aside and purposely repeating with floods of Gallic eloquence much that was common knowledge. He personally, Ambiorix, was Caesar's grateful friend. He knew it was hopeless to attempt revolt. He did not desire to do so. He had been forced by popular pressure and by the example of all Gaul. Every legion had been separately attacked on this very day. A huge band of Germans was already over the Rhine and two days' march away. The fate of the Romans, thus cut off in small units, was hopeless. Yet if Sabinus would march out to join Cicero or Labienus, Ambiorix could control his men to let them pass. The Eburones would thus be freed by the retreat of the legion, while Ambiorix would be secretly conscious of having deserved well of Caesar.

Arpineius reported all these words to Sabinus, and a hot debate took place in the middle of the camp, attended by

all the officers whatever their rank down through centurion. It was held in the open as being larger than the
quarters of the Legate, which were not yet finished. The
common soldiers, though clustered at a distance, were not
able to hear what was being said. They could, however,
see that from the first their officers were deeply divided.

Cotta and the senior centurions pointed out that the
legion's fortifications were already stout enough to withstand any number of Germans. They had their provisions
and they had their orders. Let them stand firm. Sabinus,
however, was aware that a prolonged assault by superior
numbers must in the end carry their camp, and he did not
imagine that relief would be forthcoming. In fact he pre-
sumed that Caesar had already left for Italy, it being unlikely that so vast an outbreak would have occurred before he had done so. That such an outbreak had in fact
occurred he was convinced, for the Eburones were too
small and weak a tribe to have risen alone. Unless therefore the legion bestirred itself at once, it would be hopelessly shut in by the coming of the Germans. By taking
advantage of Ambiorix's offer now, they could reach the
nearest encampment. They must make all speed.

Neither party could convince the other one, and the
debate went on with much heat. At one point Sabinus
raised his voice deliberately to let the common soldiers
know that their fate was at stake. Yet though he played
in this way for popularity, the chief centurions and Cotta
stood firm to what they thought their duty. At last the
conference broke off, to the consternation of the officers
of the legion, who now represented to both leaders that
the safety of all depended on an agreement. Either course
if resolutely pursued might save them. A quarrel was
hopeless.

Thus urged, both consented to argue again, and still disagreed. The wrangle went on for hours until at midnight Cotta, greatly distressed, was forced to yield to his superior. Orders were issued at once to march at dawn. The common soldiers, already on tenterhooks, spent what remained to them of the night packing their goods or arguing among themselves about the decision which had been obtained with such evident doubt and delay. Then sleepless, encumbered with baggage, gloomy, uncertain, they trailed out of their camp in a long column, pinning their hopes of safety on Ambiorix.

They got as far as two miles. The Gauls had taken position at both ends of a valley through which the legion must pass. Here very easily they cut them off from either exit and engaged them with great advantage of ground. Titurius Sabinus, they say, lost his head and ran up and down trying to rally the men, yet in such patent confusion that the sight of him made matters worse. Cotta, meanwhile, drew up the men under his immediate command, while other gallant officers did the same. The order was given to abandon the baggage and form a square. These were the right tactics, to be sure, but they further disheartened our men and encouraged the Gauls. Instead of straggling after plunder as might have been hoped, our enemies called to each other that the spoils would be there later on. They closed in on the legion.

Once formed in some sort of order, our men fought hard for survival. They were, however, too heavily armed to charge far uphill. The Gauls in front of them merely scattered out of harm's way, while those behind them and on every side showered darts and stones on their dense mass. Thus taking some toll, but suffering far more, the Romans struggled from dawn till two o'clock. Cotta,

fighting in the ranks with the common men, was shouting
to them for the hundredth time to come on when a sling-
shot caught him in the mouth and smashed his jaw and
mangled his lips with broken teeth. Yet he fought, blood
dripping down his chin and over his armor.

At two o'clock Sabinus sent the interpreter once more
to Ambiorix, asking for quarter. Ambiorix answered that
he hoped he might prevail on his men, but first Sabinus
must come in person to ask for terms. He pledged his
honor that the general's life at least should be respected.
At this, Sabinus prepared to go and summoned Cotta to
come with him. But for the last time Cotta, mumbling
through his broken lips, refused. He would rather die.
Sabinus ordered the senior officers and centurions to go
with him. They advanced to meet Ambiorix. All were
commanded to throw their weapons down, and Ambiorix
embarked on a long harangue, in the course of which the
Gauls kept pressing closer in. Very soon they lost their
patience. The waiting legion saw a swirl about their general and his officers. Swords were raised upon them. There
were cries as the mob threshed about. It was very soon
over. Leaving the bodies they had treacherously slain,
the mass of the Gauls raised their war cry and fell once
more in full force on the leaderless legion.

Here many died, including Lucius Cotta, fighting like
a lion to the last. A very small remnant with the Eagle in
their midst broke out of the valley and made their way
back to the camp, not so much pursued as borne along in a
tumult of blood-maddened Gauls. The standard-bearer
was cornered outside the rampart. He threw the Eagle
over the wall and died in the ditch. A few hundreds defended the ramparts till night. Then, seeing that morning would make an end of them, they killed each other to

the last man. A few others escaped from the valley somehow and got through the forest to Titus Labienus's
encampment, which they discovered in peace and unaware. The universal uprising with which Ambiorix had
terrified Sabinus had not existed.

I myself was at this time with Quintus Cicero about
fifty miles from Sabinus among the Nervii and their dependent tribes. I was by now an old hand. Winter quarters were tedious at the best of times, but this particular
winter gave promise of being more tiresome than usual.
I was somewhat of a favorite with Quintus Cicero because
of my literary endeavors. Our common interests should
have enlivened our dull days, and yet already I was beginning to find him slightly trying. Cicero was uncertain
of himself in command, and though competent, he was
apt to interfere too much. He was quite good company,
but preferred reading his own writings to me without
listening to mine. He was something of a hypochondriac
it seemed to me, always fussing about his digestion or his
headache, complaints which did not arouse my sympathy.
All in all, I had no great opinion of our commander, though
the actual business of building and fortifying the camp
went on in routine fashion because the centurions and
officers all knew their business. Woodcutting parties went
out every day, and carpenters were busy. Tents were taken
down one by one and huts erected. The local tribes delivered grain. Drilling was performed on schedule. Nothing warned us that Sabinus was besieged, was fighting and
dying. Even the arrival of Ambiorix, riding headlong from
the scene of his triumph to arouse his powerful neighbors,
passed unnoticed.

Our only warning was a sudden shout. The cohort on
guard had sighted Gauls swarming up to attack. Our men

closed the gates and sounded the alarm. The woodcutting detachment presumably was lost, but in that moment we had no thought for it. We jumped up, horribly startled, to rush from what we were doing and man the walls. Few of us were armed, and every man's position seemed at the opposite end of camp from his equipment. People collided with one another, running desperately in every direction at once. Above the confusion, the insistent sound of the trumpet was echoed and defied by the Gallic yell.

There was no panic, yet we nearly lost the camp in those first moments. To be sure, we had some minutes from the time we first saw the Gauls coming on; but no one had leisure to decide from which direction the weight of the onslaught would fall. The Gauls for their part, having achieved surprise, were mad to take our camp. They came upon us from all directions at once, so that there could be no question of assembling or directing reserves. We fought where blind chance or duty had directed us, hearing the conflict going on behind our backs and never knowing whether the enemy had not burst through somewhere else.

I do not remember what Cicero did at this time. I was too busy to notice, and for the moment our general could be of little use. It was each man for himself and for his company. We beat them in the end, and they pulled sullenly back from our ditch to encamp around us. It was clear we were blockaded, but Cicero now very briskly called for volunteers to take a message to Caesar. He was lavish with promises of reward, and several daring persons stole out of the camp after dark to try their luck.

The rest of us were not idle. Cicero was energetic. He seemed to have forgotten his finicking ways in the excitement. Parts of the rampart were not finished yet. We

needed wicker screens against the enemy's stones, stakes
pointed and hardened in the fire, siege javelins, towers for
mounting our artillery and posting our men. A hundred
and twenty towers were hastily made that very first night
and placed in position. Luckily we had plenty of wood
in the camp piled up for the contruction of our buildings.
If we had not, we should have torn our shelters down; but
this would have taken longer. Even the sick and wounded
were pressed into this work, and by the morning we were
weary, yet better prepared to face the day.

The Nervians, who had the chief command, now asked
for a conference and obtained it. All their arguments were
the same as those used on Sabinus, with the addition that
Ambiorix was with them to witness to that legion's destruction. Cicero's messengers had all been caught and killed.
Gaul was up in arms. Yet if Cicero would leave his winter quarters and go somewhere else, the Nervii would
be glad not to molest him.

Cicero's dyspepsia and ills of various sorts were now
forgotten, but he did not look well. The exhaustion of
the day and the night had told on his physical resources.
He had, however, a dignity of his own and informed the
Nervians it was not the custom of the Roman People
to accept terms from their enemies. If the Gauls would
lay down their arms, they might send representatives to
Caesar, and Cicero would intercede for them.

We were all of us proud of our commander now, but
the necessity of fighting by day and working all night soon
told on our strength. Our numbers decreased in sinister fashion, while those of the enemy if anything swelled
as the rebellion spread outward. None of the messengers
which Cicero continued to send out had got away. After
the first ones, the enemy brought their captives out in

front of our ramparts and there tortured them to death. This discouraged volunteers, and indeed the task seemed utterly hopeless.

Next the Nervii, wearied of direct assault, commenced great siegeworks, which they had learned how to construct from the Romans. They had not proper tools, and it was almost comic to see them digging with their swords and carrying earth in their cloaks. None of us, however, laughed at the sight. The Nervian numbers were so fantastic that they surrounded us with a wall ten feet high and three miles in circumference within three hours, besides digging a trench fifteen feet broad in front of it. Next they began seige approaches with ramps and towers, at which they were clumsy and slow. Yet the towers moved nearer.

On the seventh day, the towers were almost ready to be brought up to touch our rampart. Men inside them could look right over our wall with nothing to stop them save our wickerwork shelters there. It was a fine day with a stiff breeze blowing. The Gauls had prepared themselves pellets of heated clay which they began to lob over from slings which they had protected with metal linings. Presently the roofs of our huts, which were thatched in Gallic fashion, began to smolder. They burst into flames, and the breeze spread the fire. With a tremendous shout, the enemy rolled up their towers and their sheds, brought up their ladders, and flung themselves into the assault. Behind us flames crackled and roared, even in some places reaching out to scorch the defenders on the wall. Our baggage, our stores, our reserves of vital weapons, even our very wounded men were burning up. We had not anyone to spare or even a moment in which we could glance back and see the damage. The enemy crowded so

thick beneath our ramparts that the ditch was filled with
their dead, for those on the outskirts pressed against those
in front and massed them together.

That was a terrible day. What saved us from utter destruction was the wind which, though it fanned the flames,
blew them all in one direction. Buildings to windward
escaped, and with them luckily adequate supplies to maintain us. Red-eyed armorers worked desperately night
after night to patch old weapons.

Our struggle could not go on. Cicero was swaying on
his feet and could now keep no food down. He did not
complain, but the soldiers implored him to rest. Many of
us were in no better case, but sick or wounded we struggled to our feet at every alarm. None of our messengers
to Caesar had the slightest luck in getting through. Gauls
seem alike to us, but they distinguish themselves from one
another with ease. Each separate district, each tribe, almost, has its dialect or accent. Fortunately it happened
that with us in the camp was one single Nervian chief who
had fled to us at the beginning of the siege because of a
quarrel with his rivals. This man by no means dared to
trust himself outside our walls, but he had brought with
him one or two slaves and attendants whose appearance
was less widely known. Now by persuasion of Cicero
himself, one of these servants was induced by lavish promises to volunteer. He had the message bound under the
lashings of his spear, and so departed.

Caesar at Amiens received this two days afterwards at
five in the afternoon. Within a few moments orders
were speeding to Marcus Crassus, elder brother of young
Publius. Marcus had not gone with his father because
he was holding a magistracy at Rome. He had come out
to serve with Caesar and was now commanding a legion

twenty-five miles away. He marched at once. By nine
next morning, his outriders were already in Caesar's camp.
By this time Gaius Fabius had also received word and was
marching to converge on Caesar's route. Caesar directed
Marcus Crassus to remain in Amiens, where the army's
siege train, chief granary, public records, Gallic hostages,
and general arsenal were stored. He himself with a single
legion advanced with all possible speed to make junction
with Fabius. He had ordered Labienus to meet him if he
could do so. By now, however, the survivors from Sabinus's camp had reached Labienus with news of what was
going on. Indutiomarus and the Treveri, who were really
at the bottom of the whole uprising, were threatening to
fall on Labienus. He thought it madness to leave the protection of his camp and try to join Caesar.

Labienus's judgment was sound, though Caesar with
two legions was by no means as strong as he had wished
to be. He marched notwithstanding, and he sent a Gaul
ahead to deliver a message. It was easier to slip in than to
slip out, but the man was afraid to tempt his luck too far.
He fastened Caesar's message to the thong of his spear and
hurled it at our ramparts.

His weapon stuck in one of our towers. We generally
collected these spears at the end of the day to use ourselves. It happened, however, that this one was too low
down to be easily reached. Our men were tired, and it
stayed there for two days, its message flapping in the
breeze in sight of both armies.

Finally we hauled it up and saw what was there. Caesar
had written in Greek, since some of the Gauls can read
Latin. Cicero paraded those of us who could still stand
and read it to us. We cheered him hoarsely. Within the
hour, men on our towers caught sight of Caesar's beacons.

The Gauls were aware of them too, and they gave up their siege to march against Caesar. For our part, we were too exhausted to attempt any sally. Posting guards, we flung ourselves down anyhow, in the standing buildings, on the blackened ground, at the foot of the ramparts, and slept as we were in our armor with shields and helmets beside us.

On the second day after that, the beaten army of the Gauls was flying through the woods, and Caesar was with us. He complimented us all, especially Cicero and those who had performed individual feats. He would take us, he promised, to rest at Amiens for the whole of the winter.

News spreads very rapidly in Gaul, where they have a system of relaying it by shouts from village to village. At three in the afternoon on the very same day that he scattered the Nervii, Caesar had entered our camp. Before midnight nearly sixty miles away the friendly Remi were shouting at the gates of Labienus's camp to tell him of it. News also reached Indutiomarus, who had timed his attack on Labienus for next day. On hearing the tidings, he turned away and took his people home.

Disturbances had died down, and winter was on us. Caesar summoned deputations of chiefs to Amiens, where he promised, threatened, or judged. Only the Remi among the Belgians and the Aedui among the Gauls had been untouched by disloyal intrigue. One felt a muttering which went all up and down Gaul. Among the Treveri Indutiomarus still sat, unpunished so far, yet awaiting the vengeance of Caesar when it should be spring. He did not intend to suffer passively. Treveran envoys were across the Rhine, busy boasting that Sabinus's detachment had been half of Caesar's strength. Indutiomarus was trying to tempt Germans over by promises, to hire them for cash. The Germans, however, had been beaten twice and were not in a mood to court destruction. Disappointed, Indutiomarus began to drill his own troops and to attract outlaws and desperate men from all over Gaul by promising money. In very early spring he once more became active against Labienus, whom he hoped to destroy before Caesar could move. He did not, however, make an attack. Caution was so ingrained in his nature that a sudden action was beyond him. He with his cavalry roamed around our camp, exchanging insults with our men, now and then throwing weapons, studying the lie of the ground and our fortifications. Every day he grew bolder and more insolent, awaiting his moment.

He reckoned without Labienus, who was also a bold man, decisive, one who bore grudges and was known as a hard man to cross. Indutiomarus had threatened too long and had defied us too much. Labienus was prepared to make an end. He accordingly made dispositions with secrecy and skill and launched very suddenly a cavalry attack. The Gauls scattered, as he had known they would. He had instructed his men to let all others go, but to be sure to kill Indutiomarus. He had even offered a large reward for the chief's head, which was duly brought to him. Indutiomarus, pursued by all our men at once, had been caught at the ford of the river. Thereafter, at least for the moment, it became quiet in Gaul.

2

Caesar had benefited both Ambiorix and his tribe. They had repaid us by the blackest treachery. Yet my own part in our revenge troubles me yet. If the screams of the dying and the swollen bodies of the dead affected Caesar himself, he gave no sign. He knew that only by fearful punishment could he quell the spirit of rebellion. He must, moreover, have been already aware that far greater issues might soon depend on his mastery of Gaul. For Marcus Crassus had gone to carve out an empire in the East, and it is doubtful whether his success would have been more dangerous to Caesar than his tragic death became. Three masters might be held in equilibrium at Rome. Between two, there must be war. This therefore may be called a miserable summer for me, for Caesar, for Quintus Cicero, who lost by a blunder the splendid reputation he had won the preceding winter. But above everything, it was terrible for Ambiorix and his people.

AMBIORIX, KING of the Eburones, was a tall, lean, fair barbarian with a reputation among his kind as a swordsman and a hunter. His tribe lay scattered through the wild and broken country which is called the forest of the Ardennes and lies between the Rhine and the Meuse. It was a land of isolated villages where peasants battled with the wolf, the boar, and the lynx, showing scant interest in the affairs of their more powerful neighbors. Ambiorix himself, however, was a man of ambition, which is to say that to the qualities of savage independence which his people possessed, Ambiorix added a very large measure of vanity. After his exploit of destroying Sabinus with his legion, Ambiorix was for a considerable while drunk with success. Minstrels were busy with his deeds. Envoys were boasting to the Germans across the Rhine that half of Caesar's army had been exterminated. Among the Nervii, Ambiorix was feted like a hero. Indutiomarus and the Treveri vowed to attack Labienus as soon as they dared. The distant Belgians near the Seine, though directly in Caesar's power, were known to be restive. Among the Carnutes, the king whom Caesar had set to rule there had been murdered. A general uprising must open the campaign year of 53. Ambiorix might possibly aspire to command it in chief.

Ambiorix retired to the fastnesses of his wild country for the winter, a gay winter of feasting and clashing of swords on shields, while the snow-clad passes of the Ardennes cut him off to a large extent from news. Some messengers came through, however; while as the spring appeared, there were more. It was hardly noticed at first that the news was all bad. Caesar had sworn an oath that he would neither shave nor cut his hair until he had taken revenge. This was matter for laughter. Less laughable was it that he had fallen on the Nervii in dead of winter when his legions ought to have been immobilized. Since it was not possible to get their own army together before spring, the hapless Nervii had been driven out of their homes and in large numbers had perished of cold and starvation. They had submitted. Meanwhile, the Germans had not been impressed by the boastful claims of Ambiorix and his friend Indutiomarus. Word had come through to them that Caesar, so far from being weakened by his loss, was stronger than ever. In place of the legion and a half which had been destroyed, he was recruiting three. The Germans, who had been defeated on several occasions by Caesar, had no appetite for facing him again. They would send no help to the Belgians.

This last was dreadful news. Ambiorix concealed it from his friends and to a certain extent from himself.

Without the Germans, it would seem impossible to drive out Caesar. Perhaps, however, another success of some sort would change their minds. On the heels of these speculations there followed the death of Indutiomarus outside Labienus's camp. His tribe, the Treveri, though still more or less in revolt, would take no action in future unless attacked. Without the Treveri and Indutiomarus, Ambiorix could do nothing.

He put a good face on disaster, telling his people that their country was too remote, too wild and rugged for Caesar to campaign in. They would defend it to the death, and presently others would come to their aid. His personal retainers, who formed as it were his court, drank deep to him and vowed to protect him with their lives. But since the Romans did not appear, they spent their time in hunting.

Spring faded into summer. Caesar was everywhere while the corn in the fields was yet green. In very early spring he called a Council of Gaul at Paris, where he forced it to investigate the conspiracy of the Belgians in those parts. Unwilling and almost with outrage, the Council lent authority to proceedings against men who had indeed conspired but who had not been caught with arms in their hands. No demonstration of Caesar's military power brought home to them with equal force that the good old days were gone and Gallic chieftains were no longer free to take part as they pleased in the game of factions. As soon, however, as the grass was fit for forage, Caesar marched with his army for the Treveri and other tribes still in revolt. But the Eburones and Ambiorix himself he left alone.

Ambiorix waited, uneasily now, yet half reassured. Caesar was all around him, first on the lower Rhine, then on the upper. He had bridged the Rhine once more to teach the Germans not to interfere. In fact he had circled the Eburones on all sides, but the actual country of the Ardennes he had so far not entered.

"He dare not," Ambiorix boasted. "Ours is a country for ambush, not for open fighting. Caesar would be lucky to struggle out again once we had entrapped him."

He spoke to his retainers and his kinsmen assembled in his own hall. He had not called together the fighters of his tribe for the obvious reason that he could not provision them indefinitely. By retreating to this particular lodge deep in the woods, he counted on receiving ample warning before Caesar's army had advanced more than a mile or two over his borders. Then he would call out his folk and fall upon Caesar in a place of his own choosing.

Thus Ambiorix planned, and thus he boasted. His hall was a large one, built under trees for coolness and surrounded by outbuildings of every sort — barns, stables, women's quarters — huts of wattle and clay forming a considerable courtyard protected by a gate and a rough palisade. In this courtyard a dog began to bark. A man called out. There was a confused sound of galloping hoofs. Women screamed. As those in the hall leaped to their feet and snatched at weapons on the walls, Ambiorix's young son, a boy of ten, appeared in the doorway yelling, "It is the Romans!"

It was indeed a Roman cavalry party of about eight hundred strong whom Caesar had ordered to push on ahead of his army, light no fires to betray their coming, let no one escape to carry warning, and question all prisoners on the whereabouts of Ambiorix. Penetrating deep into the country undiscovered, they had been able to approach the house unseen through the surrounding woods.

Some were already battling with retainers at the entrance
to the yard, while others were fanning out to surround
the place completely.

There was not a moment to be lost. Ambiorix's household, including women and children, hardly amounted to
two hundred persons all told. One of these, however, had
kept his head. Instead of joining in the struggle round
the gate, he had run to the stable and dragged out the
nearest horse. "Quick! This way!" Ambiorix leaped
on it and sped out a little side gate. Bareheaded, grasping
the mane of his bridleless horse, and madly urging it with
the flat of his sword, he vanished into the forest. No
quarter was given, and the rest of his people — men,
women, and children — all perished. Bereft of his supporters, Ambiorix sent instructions for everyone in the
tribe to shift for himself.

Having subdued the tribes all about and deprived the
Eburones of refuge, Caesar advanced to exterminate their
race and name. He brought his army to the spot where
Sabinus's camp had been and where the walls were still
standing. He had with him one of his new legions, the
Fourteenth, not yet fit to be trusted in battle. This he
left in camp to look after the baggage, giving command of
it to Quintus Cicero, whom he instructed not to allow
these inexperienced soldiers outside the walls. He divided
the rest of his army into three columns, assured Cicero
that he would be back in a week, and advanced to show
Gaul how terrible he could be when he was angered.

Caesar marked his trail with fire and slaughter, but the
valleys of the Ardennes are hard to ransack, save by splitting into small parties. Caesar therefore bethought himself of how to save his men from ambush and decided to
let the Gauls do part of the work. He invited whoever

would of the neighboring tribes to join him and share in the plunder.

There are always feuds in Gaul. No admiration or envy of the deed of the Eburones saved them now. Once given permission to fight and harry freely, the tribes closed in. Men were hunted up and down those wooded valleys as though by wolves. They took refuge in the marshes of the lower Rhine and were butchered there. They tried to hide themselves on sandy spits in the river's mouth and were tracked down and killed. The whole of their country was filled with blackened huts, uprooted crops, the swollen bodies of men, women, and children left to rot.

Through this desolation, up and down the length of this wild land, Caesar hunted Ambiorix. Sometimes the Gaul was but a day ahead of his pursuer. Sometimes men had seen him pass within the hour, red-eyed and ragged, bent over the mane of his horse as though no longer able to sit upright, his fair hair and beard dark with dirt, his glance ever behind him. Some even when questioned would say, "He is here. He is with us," and look round to see that he had gone. Sometimes Ambiorix rode alone. More often four horsemen were with him, all the servants who were left from the days of his greatness, the only people in the length and breadth of Gaul he dared trust with his life.

Thus Caesar postponed the conquest of Britain and took his revenge, while Quintus Cicero lay uneasily cooped up with the Fourteenth Legion in the ill-omened camp of the dead Sabinus. Possibly for some reason connected with this spot, a strange thing occurred. One of our legionaries saw a vision.

There are always soothsayers in camp. It is of course

well known that dreams and omens have a very remarkable power of foreshadowing the future. Any soldier who must risk his life almost daily is susceptible in the highest degree to supernatural warnings. Playing on the credulity of the ignorant, charlatans infested us and were ignored by Caesar as long as they kept their predictions in bounds and did not prophesy defeat or spread alarm. But amid the trickeries of such despicable folk, there occurred occasionally a genuine omen, always hard to distinguish until after the event which it foretold. There were, for instance, occasional men in our ranks who claimed to possess second sight. Such people are awkward to deal with because they are sincere. On this occasion, a man claimed to have had a vision concerning the defeat and death of Caesar.

Cicero took cognizance of the matter at once. He was not, like Caesar, completely skeptical about such things. He rather tended to collect accounts of miracles and portents. On this occasion, however, he was soldier enough to understand that such a prophecy was untimely. The Fourteenth was very raw, and its morale was shaky. Caesar had left it alone in this ill-omened place. It would not be possible for our veteran legions to conceive of Caesar in defeat. The Fourteenth, however, might very easily be thrown into a panic. Cicero therefore interviewed the soldier in person with the intention of ridiculing his story. Actually, however, he found it curious.

It seemed at first telling that the soldier's vision had merely concerned itself with the death of Sabinus. He had been standing, or so he said, in the ranks of a defeated legion. He did not remember where he stood in the line, who was with him, or any of the detail of wounded, dead, or despairing men. He only knew there had been fighting for a very long time, that they were cut off, and that the general was going out with his officers to negotiate surrender. He said that he watched them, knowing as he did so that they would not return alive and that the army would be left leaderless and so would perish.

Hearing this rigmarole, Cicero with some indignation demanded to know how he dared connect such a story with Caesar's death when all knew the end of Sabinus had come after such a fashion. The answer startled him. Because, so the soldier said, he had watched the general ride out across the plain, and his cloak had been scarlet.

This made the whole story peculiar indeed. No mere Legate such as Sabinus had been wore the scarlet cloak. Besides, the mention of a plain seemed strange. The soldier described it as rolling, hilly in the distance, sandy, treeless, and covered with coarse grass or scrub. Nothing more different from the wooded ravines of the Ardennes seemed possible. With some relief Cicero pointed this out, derided the story, and shut the man's mouth by threatening a lashing. Yet Cicero himself found the tale very strange, and some months later when news came trickling in from the east, he sent for the man again — but by then he was dead. Thus any details which he might have been afraid to add were never discovered. But Cicero believed, and it seemed likely, that the man had been a genuine seer. For this is the story which came much later to our ears about Marcus Crassus.

While Caesar prepared to smite the Eburones, Marcus Crassus on the other side of the world had crossed the Euphrates and marched out onto the hot, dry Parthian plain in search of glory. He had with him seven legions, four thousand horse, and as many light-armed soldiers; and he met the Parthians — a little more than a third of his own force — near a place called Carrhae. Here he discovered facts which he might, perhaps, have learned from Pompey. The Parthians are horsemen, their nobles heavily armed with metal-studded shields and mighty spears. The rest are archers. Crassus formed his infantry in a square which very easily sufficed for repulsing charges, yet made a massed target for the arrows which the Parthians rained in upon them without intermission, having relays of fresh ammunition brought up on the backs of camels.

Seeing that his legions were being massacred where they stood, Crassus eventually called upon his son, young Publius, to charge the light-armed archers with his cavalry and put them to flight. Accordingly, Publius bore down on the Parthians with his thousand horsemen from Gaul, a few hundreds more whom he had under his command, five hundred archers, and eight cohorts of a legion to act as support if he needed any. The Parthian archers showed no desire to let Publius come to close quarters. They retreated rapidly, shooting from time to time over the rumps of their horses in a practiced and highly effective manner. Publius followed, for if he retired they would return. Unless he could come to grips and break them up, his horsemen were useless.

Thus retreating and pursuing, both vanished out of sight, for the country here was gently rolling. Crassus, meanwhile, relieved from pressure, began to edge his army towards a slope of ground and a better position. But Publius presently saw the Parthian archers wheel suddenly to left or right while the heavy cavalry on which they had retreated came up between them. Both sides crashed together with force, but the armor and weapons of the Gauls were far inferior to those of the Parthians. Publius's men fought like lions, but they died. He sent urgent messages to his father to hurry as fast as he could to the rescue. Two friends begged Publius to flee with them, for the swiftness of their horses made it probable they would escape. Publius told them no fear of death could make him leave his men to perish without him.

Meanwhile, the older Crassus marched to the rescue. The Parthians met him halfway, shouting and beating their drums and tossing their standards in the air. They came nearer, and a murmur ran down the Roman lines, while those about Crassus tried to tell him not to look. The foremost standard was the head of Publius stuck on a spear.

For all his faults, Marcus Crassus was a Roman in our noble antique mold. He rode down the ranks of his soldiers calling to them, "Oh my countrymen, this is my personal loss and matters little. The fortune and glory of Rome are safe with you." They say his voice was steady, but his face was pallid and old. A few days later when he rode out in his scarlet cloak to surrender and death, he did not care.

Thus perished Crassus, even as our soldier had seen him do. His dying tore the whole rotten fabric of Roman politics apart. For years the partnership of The Three had kept a balance. Now the scales of power held but two. Either Caesar or Pompey must weigh more. One or the other, conversely, must weigh less. With the death of Julia and the failure of their common hopes, the rival generals were no longer in any sense allies. Now might Pompey build up his forces in Spain, gather legions on the pretext of going to Parthia to avenge Crassus, and yet not

go. Now every governor of every province of Rome must
look to Caesar or to Pompey. Pompey gathered himself
at Rome and swelled in power.

For all these reasons, one might suppose that our common soldier's vision was meant as a warning to Caesar of
troubles to come. If so, it failed of its purpose. Ambiorix
was twisting and doubling through the forests of the
Eburones while Caesar was calling up the hounds. Even
a tribe of the Germans had made haste to cross the Rhine
on rafts and share in the plunder. Soon, however, they
discovered that Caesar was some way off, while all his
baggage had been left in camp under Cicero's charge and
in care of a legion which did not feel strong enough to
venture outside the walls. They concluded that to plunder this would be far more profitable than competing
with the neighboring Belgian tribes for booty among the
Eburones. They directed their horses thither.

Cicero meanwhile had passed a tedious week. There
were many pack animals in the camp which by now were
short of forage. The men of the Fourteenth complained
of the heat and the flies and of nothing to do. A considerable body of veterans on the sick list had recovered.
These pointed out that with nine legions in a small area,
no opposition, and all the neighboring Gauls out hunting
Ambiorix, there was no reason to behave as though besieged. Cicero stuck to his orders, but when seven days
were up and Caesar had not appeared, he thought it reasonable to use his own discretion. Accordingly he permitted half the legion to go out and reap the grain which
was known to be growing on the opposite slope of a hill
out of sight of the camp. The baggage animals were sent
out to feed on fresh grass, while three hundred of the re-

covered veterans marched out in a separate command to help with the harvest.

At this awkward moment, the German horsemen rode up at a gallop and tried to crash through the rear gate. There was as it happened a wood close up to the camp on this side, so that before the Germans were noticed they were almost among the traders, whose booths according to custom had been put up outside the gates along the rampart.

There was a cohort on guard, but the inexperience and clumsiness of the Fourteenth made everything harder. The alarm was sounded confusedly. There was general panic. That indestructible man, Sextius Baculus, was now the first centurion of the Twelfth. After recovering from desperate wounds which would have killed most people, he had fallen sick again, this time of that common complaint of armies, dysentery. Far from recovered, he had been lying in his tent and had not eaten for five successive days. However, hearing the tumult, he pulled himself to his feet and staggered out.

The situation was desperate. The barbarians were fighting in the gateway, and the guards were yielding ground. Baculus snatched weapons from the nearest frightened fool and rushed to the rescue, shouting hoarsely. His example encouraged other men to do the same. Many knew him, for in so small a camp a first centurion and a hero of the wars was bound to be known. If he could rise from his sickbed to fight, then they could follow. Presently Baculus was run through by a German spear and collapsed, but it had by now become a point of honor to those who fought in the gate to save his life. With furious efforts, they dragged him out from under the horses' hoofs and thrust the Germans back till the gates could be closed.

Meanwhile, the harvesting party had heard the noise and started back over the hill. But when they got in sight and saw the Germans, they did not know what to do. They understood in the abstract their battle formations, but how to get into them they did not know. The muleteers and grooms, who at this moment came tearing through their ranks, increased their confusion. Their officers and centurions, though experienced soldiers promoted from other legions, were unused to their authority and uncertain of their men. They did not know whether to dash for the camp in wedge formation or whether to seize a position on a knoll and resist where they were. The recovered veterans who were with them had no doubts. Few though they were, they charged the enemy and reached camp without the loss of a man. The grooms followed their rush. But the cohorts of the Fourteenth were in no position to do anything decisive. They were quickly surrounded and neither charged nor resisted steadily where they were. Some of their centurions, fighting like lions, brought part of them off. The rest were massacred in sight of their horrified comrades on the wall.

Luckily the Germans now drew off. It did not occur to them that they might still have captured the camp, for the Fourteenth was in a panic. The rumor that Caesar had been defeated and killed was immediately revived. The men argued this must be the case or the Germans would not have dared to attack. Even the arrival of Caesar's cavalry that night scarcely calmed their fears.

Preoccupied with this disaster, Caesar was not in a mood to be troubled with visions. Cicero, who felt himself at fault, did not wish to approach him. Besides, Caesar had not yet completed his revenge. All that rainy autumn men trampled the lands of the Eburones, burned their hamlets, ate their grain, and turned their land into a desert in which those who escaped must certainly starve. But Ambiorix eluded the Romans still in those savage woodlands.

Caesar left that country at last and encamped at Reims. The Gallic council was forced to assemble again and take more proceedings against those Belgian chiefs who had plotted rebellion. Their leader, a chief of the Carnutes called Acco, was executed by flogging in the ancient Roman way. Having thus taught the Belgians a lesson, Caesar quartered most of his legions at Sens for the winter. He himself meanwhile set out for Italian Gaul to hold the assizes.

3

PRELUDE TO AN OUTBURST 53-52 B.C.

This was an ominous winter. Though we had fearfully avenged Sabinus in the blood of the Eburones, Gaul still muttered. In the Province, wise old Caburus scented trouble coming. In the northern regions, even Commius was disaffected, so that the old quarrel between himself and Volusenus broke out anew. Caesar was not with our army. Political squabbles in Rome had reached such a pitch that government had broken down. Pompey was arming at the request of the Senate, who had proclaimed martial law. In his province of Nearer Gaul in the north of Italy, Caesar was recruiting, too. If he considered Pompey unfair to his partisans, he might just possibly cross over his border in force. That would mean civil war. Our army waited, hungering for scraps of news. Gauls wildly exaggerated every rumor drifting across the Alps, and they told each other that a great opportunity was near.

All this portended a series of uprisings. We never imagined that the Gauls would unite under a single chief. We knew Vercingetorix as a young man widely beloved, but deeply suspected by the elders of his own tribe. If we

*ever thought of him as a hero, it was in the easy fashion of
the old times which we despised — the fashion of hunting
and boasting and swaggering in bright clothes. It never
occurred to us that he had the eloquence, the craft, the
force, the understanding of war which would lift him
suddenly above his seniors in Gaul. Vercingetorix came
into our lives like a meteor appearing we hardly knew
from where. In one brief summer, he flashed across our
sky and then vanished, the great man of Gaul.*

GAIUS VALERIUS CABURUS had aged during six years of
war. He seemed to have shriveled a little, though perhaps
this was due to his sitting cross-legged in the Gallic fashion
on the fresh-strewn rushes of his floor. The great hall of
his country house served his people as kitchen, banqueting
hall, armory, and even to some extent storehouse or sleeping place. There was always bustle in the hall, always
smoke and smell of cooking. Caburus now no longer was
outside among his people all day, while the smaller rooms
in winter were cold for an old man, and also lonely. It
had in fact become understood that a certain corner of
the great hall was private for the master, who kept his
eyes on his people and called them over as he pleased.
When, as at present, he sat and talked to his son, they
did not disturb him.

"Were Procillus to recover from his wound," Caburus

said, "he could still not lead the Helvians this year. And I foresee trouble."

Dumnotaurus tugged at his long mustaches. He envied his father his ability to live with Roman and Gaul alike. He himself felt easy with neither. He pretended to be at heart a free Gaul, yet among the Arverni he was only a Helvian chief, far less considerable in himself than because of his father's Roman connections. His brother Procillus had lain all winter on his bed, and it seemed doubtful if he would ever get up. Dumnotaurus was thus effectively the Helvian leader, and this at a moment when the resentment of the Gallic chiefs against Caesar had almost persuaded them to concerted revolt. How could Dumnotaurus join them? His lands lay in the Province, and were he to try and rouse his father's men, they would not follow. For his cousin Vercingetorix, defiance was easy. Even Caesar had never marched his legions through the highland plateau of the Arverni. He had contented himself with a submission from its chiefs and a tribute of grain. That was very wild country. If Vercingetorix had risen five years back, Dumnotaurus might have followed. But Vercingetorix at that time had been very young and was suspect by the chiefs of his tribe. Now both were older and in their different ways wiser. Yet having in the past won the confidence of his cousin, Dumnotaurus did not know how to draw back.

"There has been a murder in Rome," Caburus said, seeing that his son sat silent. "A political murder. It has alarmed the Senate into decreeing a mass levy throughout Italy. Caesar is arming, meanwhile, in the north. I do not know whether or not this means civil war."

Dumnotaurus nodded. "Wild tales are abroad. It is said Caesar has been summoned to Rome in this emergency.

It is said he will be too busy to think of Gaul this spring. And without Caesar in Gaul . . .   There has been a meeting of chiefs. A secret meeting."

"You attended such a thing?" asked Caburus aghast. "You will ruin us all. But you took no oath?"

"I took no oath," Dumnotaurus told him frowning, "because I was not summoned to go. I have no power in free Gaul. I do not know what the chiefs talked of or what they resolved, but their standards were bound into a sheaf."

The old man shook his head in despair. The binding together of the tribal standards was an ancient ceremony never resorted to, save when tribes vowed to live and die as one.

"It was the execution of Acco set them on," Dumnotaurus remarked, peering gloomily into the smoke of the hall as though he might find there a clue to how much he should say. "It is one thing for a chief to die in a good fight. It is another to watch him beaten to death without being able to utter a word of protest. None knew who might be next. Meanwhile, Ambiorix is hunted through the hills like a mad dog. Many knew Ambiorix."

Caburus sighed. "I did advise Caesar that to execute Acco publicly would be a mistake. But Caesar is greatly changed by success. He does not require my advice."

Dumnotaurus glanced at him, startled. "I never heard you say anything against Caesar before now."

Caburus stroked his beard and seemed to reflect. "My son," he said slowly, "I was a friend of Diviciacus, who in his life was the wisest man in Gaul. He knew that the Romans must be our masters, and so do I. Yet do you imagine that no one but yourself perceives they despise us? I have suffered injustice in my day and often have

envied the free chiefs of Long-haired Gaul. I have seen,
however, how much more prosperous are we in the
Province. Have you considered how easily Caesar feeds
his army in Gaul, hardly consuming more grain than used
to be destroyed by the tribes raiding each other? Or do
you suppose that if the Romans were driven out, the yoke
of the Germans would be found easier to bear? Ask the
Sequani if they have forgotten King Ariovistus yet. As
for this binding of the standards together, I have seen
many such occasions, and yet how much unity or strength
has any brought Gaul?"

"A great leader might unify Gaul," Dumnotaurus suggested.

His father sighed. "Who ever commanded the chiefs
of Long-haired Gaul except by force?"

Dumnotaurus looked at the ground and gave no answer.

"You can take no part in their foolishness," his father
persisted. "You are of the Province."

"I have no part as yet," the young man muttered.

"And you will not join them?"

"No."

We were quartered for that winter at Sens, which lies on
a tributary of the Seine in the country of the Senones,
excellently placed for watching the Carnutes and Parisians, while yet close to the Belgians. Caesar had quartered two legions east of us at Langres and two with the
Treveri, lest any of the exhausted Belgian tribes revolt.
The remaining six of us were in reserve under Labienus
at Sens.

There is always coming and going of a sort near winter
quarters. It does not follow that parties cannot travel,

merely because the weather is unsuitable for transporting masses of men with mules and baggage. Traders move about as they can, and local Gauls bring wares to sell, offer services for hire, or purvey news. All Gauls love gossip, and a successful piece is known to be rewarding. Besides, as I have said before, such are the jealousies between Gauls that every one of them informs on his fellows. Actually, our chief difficulty in getting news is that Gauls are credulous and are not above making up tales to suit their purpose. When, however, a number of people tell the same story, it generally has truth at least at bottom.

After all this time spent in Gaul, a number of us had acquaintances among the cavalry chiefs and spoke a little Gallic. It was our duty to keep ourselves informed and to pass on anything which seemed of the first importance. When rumor reached me that there had been a conference of chiefs — some said in a wood outside Paris, some said just north of the Loire — I reported as a matter of course to Labienus.

I found him angry. Labienus was a hard, efficient man who admired Caesar only at his most ruthless. Had matters been left to Labienus, either the Gauls would have revolted long since or never dared. But Caesar, as he was apt to complain, was lenient with them.

"Conference of chiefs?" he snapped. "About what? Where? With whom? You must keep your ears open, man. If there's any truth in it, half a dozen of them will soon be here to play the informer."

No one did inform on the chiefs, which was very curious. The rumor kept on coming in. This chief and that one was mentioned as having been present — or having been absent from his tribe, which might mean the same thing. No word, however, came through about what had been resolved. Presently Labienus called together all of us who knew something of it.

"What's at the bottom of this?" he demanded in his brusque way. "Have you any ideas?"

"There's an oath at the bottom of this," Volusenus drawled, unimpressed as usual. "Most of these barbarians would betray their own fathers out of sheer spite, but they have oaths they're frightened of."

"That is what I suppose," Labienus agreed. "And since Gauls will not submit to an oath unless something desperate is planned, we need to find out what it is."

"Who was present?" asked Decimus Brutus.

Everyone contributed a name or two, and the list began to sound like a roster of the chief men south of the Seine. We had no means of knowing which of these were accused out of malice and which had really been there.

"This does at least localize the trouble," Labienus remarked. "None of the Aedui and their dependents, of course, and none of the Belgians."

"I don't know about that," Basilus said. "I heard, Commius."

"*Commius!*" Labienus positively started as though someone had pricked him in the back. "The wildest guessing!"

"Commius!" echoed Volusenus almost with a chuckle. "I'd believe anything about that murdering scoundrel. Wait till I catch him!"

Labienus shrugged this off. Volusenus's private feud with Commius was well known. Something, however, had come into my own mind. "I heard Commius was absent from his tribe," I ventured, "but I thought nothing of it. Caesar gave him the kingship over the Atrebates, and

this year he added also the Morini. Commius owes us too
much. Besides, we all know him . . ."

We all did know Commius. It was not likely that he
would sit in his kingdom all winter long. He must be running here and there, sowing ideas. Only it seemed in-
credible that these could involve any harm to the Romans,
on whom he depended.

"Commius rules the Morini," Decimus Brutus said,
thinking this through aloud. "And the Atrebates. That
is to say, he holds the coast all round about Boulogne. His
connections in Britain, as all of us there saw, are influential. There is no doubt Commius is disappointed in Caesar
because he did not pursue the conquest of Britain."

Labienus still shook his head. "He depends upon us
for the kingship that he has. Commius is no fool."

"There was Tasgetius who depended on us, too, and
his people murdered him. It might appear wiser to lead
one's countrymen in rebellion and be a popular hero."

"I must have more evidence," Labienus declared. "But
I swear if Commius has played the traitor, I'll have no
mercy on him."

"Nor I," Volusenus said in my ear. "It will be a pleasure."

To our own surprise, there was more evidence, though
we might have known that Commius of all men was never
discreet. We never did learn whether he had attended the
mysterious meeting, or if so what he had done and said.
He was, however, going about among his Belgian neighbors dropping dark hints and making approaches which
could not be mistaken. None of the Belgians had much
spirit left for revolt after last summer, though there were
hotheads in every tribe as there always were. To these
Commius darkly promised some mighty deed. In general

also he proclaimed that there was civil war in Rome and that certainly Caesar would not cross the Alps this year. He put his arm round men's shoulders and talked confidentially about the poor generalship of Caesar's lieutenants.

Labienus was bitterly angry, the more so because Commius alarmed him. If a conspiracy in Gaul had really been formed, it was all-important to prevent it from spreading to the Belgians. Caesar had never faced both halves of Gaul in revolt at once. Commius's influence was great because of his nature, and his position as Caesar's former friend would tend to increase it. Chiefly, however, Labienus was disgusted by the low treachery of the man, who with no other motive as far as we could see but his own self-interest was trying to betray those who had been his friends. Had it been possible to get Commius into his power, Labienus would have executed him as we did Acco. Commius, however, was much too wily to trust himself at Sens. He sent excuses.

Volusenus now took affairs into his own hands and went to Labienus with a proposal to murder Commius, who as he always maintained had tried to kill him. Labienus, or so Volusenus told me, agreed in an instant that the treacherous dog deserved no better. He doubted, however, if anyone could be persuaded to do it.

"I'll do it myself if you will give me leave," Volusenus said.

Labienus started at that, for he had considered the hiring of some Gaul and not the open use of soldiers in so dubious a matter. It would not look well.

"What matter how it looks?" Volusenus told him. "It will frighten the Belgians. If the conspiracy that we suspect is growing throughout Gaul, we must take care of ourselves. Commius deserves nothing."

Labienus agreed in the end. He was a bold, hard man,
concerned more with results than with method. If what
he contemplated was not too savory, he could defend
himself by talking of Commius's deserts. He sent to Commius to say that if the chief could not come to Sens, he
would like him to meet an officer for conference. The
situation in Gaul disquieted him. He had heard rumors
which he wished to discuss with his faithful friend. If
Commius would appoint a time and place, he would send
an envoy.

Much more passed in this style. There is no doubt that
Commius realized he was not trusted. Conference details
were arranged with a formal care, so many for escort on
each side and a truce to be observed. It might have been
a meeting between two parties already at war.

"His curiosity," Volusenus assured us, "will induce
him to come." Apparently it did. Besides, our reputation
for good faith had been established by Caesar.

Labienus appointed a guard and special centurions who
volunteered for the deed. It was arranged that Volusenus
should take the chief by the hands in greeting while the
man nearest stabbed him. The rest would defend themselves against the outraged escort of Commius and bring
their leader off.

All started to go according to plan, but the centurion
was not quite quick enough. Very possibly Commius had
been suspicious. At all events, as the murderer drew his
sword out, one of the Gauls struck him and diverted the
blow. Commius could not entirely escape it because his
hands were held; and it hit him on the face, sheering
through the bridge of his nose and his cheek, so that with
a cry he dropped backwards, horribly mangled and ap-

parently dying. Both sides drew swords, but each expected the other to attack and was only anxious to get
away. Volusenus retired while the Gauls took Commius,
who by a miracle recovered from his wound after a long
illness.

The attempt made considerable stir. Commius's friends
were very angry. Labienus shrugged their accusations
off, content that the Belgians were now completely cowed.
As for Volusenus, he had taken his revenge and boasted
of it.

The mountain town of Gergovia lay on a little plateau
six hundred yards long and perhaps one third as wide. Below it, an escarpment, natural yet improved by men's
hands, dropped sheer away. Lower still, the ground descended in tumbled rock or ravine into a valley, affording
only footpaths of the most precarious sort to those who
would rather scramble up the northwest face than go
round to the steep and terraced pastures which gave access
of a kind on the southern side. Beyond the valley, crowd-
ing to be seen from Gergovia's height, the wooded hills
and rocky windswept plateaus of the Arvernian country
jostled each other to the horizon. There was a sprinkling
of snow on the bare rocks and the bare trees, up which the
lengthening shadow of the declining sun was sweeping
slowly. It was reaching to the foot of Gergovia's escarpment now. The ravine below it lay chill and colorless and
cold, though in Gergovia cattle still lowed and people
shouted. The clink of the hammers of the metal workers
for which Gergovia was famous beat an accompaniment
like the pulse of the township.

Between this silence and this bustle stood a man who
was looking north. He stood in the sunlight, above the

escarpment yet outside the wall of loose stone which served to conceal him from curious eyes in the town. He was waiting for something as the shadows crept up towards his feet and the yellow rays of the sun picked out his bracelet of gold, his torque, and the mass of red-gold hair swept back from his forehead.

This champion of Gaul in his brief hour of glory was Vercingetorix, a son of Celtillus, who had aspired to be king of the Arverni. Nothing was left of Celtillus now, save the wealth which had fired his ambition, this one son, and perhaps a distant legend or two of Arvernian glory. Both the son and his wealth were objects of suspicion to the chiefs who for many years had ruled the Arverni. As for the legend, they preferred their ease to glory. Even the Aedui had suffered from this war. Caesar had billeted his forces there. The Helvetian horde had marched right through them. Even the Remi, chief Roman supporters among the Belgian tribes, had afforded Caesar a battleground. Meanwhile the Arverni, ingloriously paying their tribute, had never seen their mountain glens defiled by invaders. The clinking hammers of Gergovia still wrought more brooches than swords. The chieftains feasted and hunted and listened to their minstrels singing their praises as though their wild, free life was undisturbed. But they watched Vercingetorix, too, the son of Celtillus.

He was a man to watch. All eyes were drawn to him by his stature, his bright mane of hair, his gorgeous costumes, his weapons, the horses he rode, and above all by something fiery in his nature. Vercingetorix had been born to lead, and Gaul to follow. At the coming of Caesar six years ago, he had been but a very young man, devoid of influence save among the other young men whom the chiefs ignored. Now he was in the prime of his life, and the tide which had once been against him ran in his favor. Gaul was tinder, and a spark might set it on fire. There was a blow to be struck in the north which might produce the spark.

A very faint, distant sound came drifting over the valley. Vercingetorix peered down into the distance, but saw nothing. This was as it should be, since he had instructed his callers to stay hidden, lest Gergovia know he waited for news. Presently the cry would be taken up if he had really heard it. Ringing distantly from the winding cleft in the hills, here it came.

"Gre . . . at mass-acre of Romans at Or-lé-ans . . . Dawn this morn-ing."

It was here. Orléans, great grain center, where Caesar had a commissary, where Roman traders wintered, Gauls came to market. . . . Dawn this morning a hundred and sixty miles away. At last the Carnutes had avenged the death of Acco, as they had sworn they would. Now all whose standards had been bound in with theirs must abide by their oath. Vercingetorix did not stay to listen again. He turned and swung himself in over the wall. A moment later his voice called out in sunlit Gergovia while the shadows crept up the scarp.

"Gre-at mass-acre of Romans at Or-lé-ans . . . Dawn this morn-ing."

Babel broke out in Gergovia, and for the first time in many years the noise of hammering ceased, and shouts of anger or defiance rose over the wall. For Vercinget-orix was calling to arms against the Romans, while the chieftains, starting from their houses in dismay, were summoning their men. No doubt Gergovia was theirs. Since the death of Celtillus, none had questioned their rule or looked elsewhere for protection. Presently as the sun's rim dipped, the clash of arms rang out. Much later by torchlight a mob of men poured out of the southern gate amidst whizzing of brickbats and yells of defiance. The chiefs of Gergovia consolidated themselves on their barren rock, while Vercingetorix stormed out to use his fiery eloquence on the Arverni.

4

THE GREAT REBEL 52 B.C.

I never knew Vercingetorix, though I had often seen him. I bought myself one of his people some years later. The man was being worked on one of our big farms and had attracted the dislike of his overseer. I was lucky to get his story. He would not have lasted much longer. As for the factions among the Aedui on which Vercingetorix so skillfully played, I knew them well. Diviciacus and Dumnorix were both dead, but the younger chieftains had mostly served with us. For cavalry we depended chiefly on Gauls, a large contingent of whom were always from the Aedui. But in the negotiations of this year I played no part. How could I have done? I fought at Bourges. I was in attendance on Caesar. I went with him on his famous march to reclaim the Aedui. Yet mine was no important role, and the hero of this summer is in any case a Gaul. Let facts speak for him.

By March, Gaul was in arms. The Orléans massacre had been the signal for the chiefs to rise, as they had sworn to do in their secret meeting. Almost every tribe was up, from the Arverni in the south as far as to the Seine, from the borders of the Aedui as far as to the Atlantic. Only the Aedui themselves and the defeated Belgian tribes adhered to Caesar. A Gallic army had been in the field this last month, but its organization took time. First Vercingetorix had made himself king of the Arverni. Other chieftains hastily summoned had elected him commander-in-chief amidst scenes of excitement such as are beloved of Gauls. They had, however, preserved their own right to sit in council, to argue, and to force their young commander to defer to their opinions. But Vercingetorix well understood when to yield, how to convince, and when to let the facts themselves speak for him.

"Already Caesar is marching on us from Sens," he reproached them. "Six weeks ago, Caesar was on the other side of the Alps. Last month he was in the Province, while all his legions were to the north of us at Sens or among the Belgians. Only the Aedui offered Caesar a safe road to join his army. We ought to have cut him off. I for my part attacked the Aedui and sent them envoys in secret as well. We have many friends among them. I urged my kinsman Lucterius to threaten the Province from its northwestern side and to tie down any troops that Caesar could gather."

"Yet you drew us off from the Aedui yourself," a chief pointed out, "to go to the rescue of the Arverni."

Vercingetorix turned on him. "Need I have done so if all your contingents had come in? The passes of the Cévennes were six feet deep in snow when Caesar burst through them and appeared in Arvernian country. He had no forces with him except the replacements he had brought from Italy. I might have dealt with him and still continued to press the Aedui, had you but been punctual. As it was, I was forced to draw off. Caesar slipped round us and, riding night and day with a picked escort, he reached his army. Now he is on the march in force. This should have been prevented."

The last free Council of Gaul looked on its commander in silence. All the chiefs knew what Vercingetorix would have done. He had already allotted fixed quotas to the tribes, not only of men, but of weapons. Some had not been delivered, or had come late. Tribesmen had decided that they did not care for a long campaign and had started to desert. Vercingetorix had ruthlessly seized on offenders, cut off an ear or gouged out an eye, and sent them home to show their fellows that he intended to be obeyed.

One or two he had even tortured publicly and burned in cages of wicker, as had been the ancient custom. Yet the chieftains had, as far as they could, protected their own and resisted discipline, hoping as usual to be successful without it. Now the time had come when tacitly they knew they must submit.

"We have to defeat Caesar's army," Vercingetorix said.

There arose a clamor at this. Very naturally those chiefs whose tribes lay in Caesar's path were for immediate battle, while those who were luckier preferred to play for time. "He will not advance very far," one chief maintained. "The grass is not green."

"He has left his baggage train and mules behind."

"But he has cavalry. Somehow his horses must eat."

"And therefore we can starve him," Vercingetorix agreed. "It is impossible, as you know, for us to face Caesar in battle. Remember the Nervii, the Helvetians, even the Germans whom we ourselves could not overcome. Nor dare we shut ourselves inside our fortified places. Caesar will take them with his siegeworks and his towers. What town has withstood him for more than a few days?"

"This time we will die rather than flee. We all vow it."

"We will starve rather than surrender our cities."

"We will not die," Vercingetorix cried. "We will starve Caesar's army. We will burn our farms and our hay. We will burn our towns. We will drive off our cattle. Let Caesar advance through a desert. As for those who lie in his path, we will remember the miseries which they must suffer for Gaul. One day we will reward them."

Never in the history of Gaul had a chieftain of one

tribe called on the men of another to sacrifice all. But Vercingetorix knew how to command his people. In him ambition was no mere greed for power. It was not even barbaric appetite for glory. All the chiefs could see that he rose above such motives and was fighting for the good old days and the freedom of Gaul. Perhaps because of his youth he did not perceive that those great times were gone forever. He hastened to pit Gallic independence and pride against the efficiency of the ruthless, cultured, and ambitious Roman. Yet Vercingetorix was no naïve barbaric hero. Where single-mindedness and loftiness of spirit did not suffice, he knew how to use the arts of propaganda. Nor did he scruple to descend to bribery in the good cause. Dazzled, bemused, bought, or coerced, the intransigent chieftains of Gaul followed for a brief span their natural leader.

It was the Bituriges who lay on the borders of the Aedui, to whom Caesar was attempting to bring aid, lest he have no friends left in Gaul. The Bituriges therefore were urgently reminded that defeat meant death for themselves and slavery for their women and children. Thus inflamed, they fired twenty towns and countless outlying farms in Caesar's path. Smoke hung in the air over many miles. Poor people, laden with their wretched goods or driving their cattle, trudged off to whatever safety their neighbors could offer. A wail of misery went up from the whole land, but the Bituriges were powerless to check what they had begun in sight of the army. One city only they begged for on their knees before all the chieftains of Gaul. They begged for Bourges.

Bourges was the fairest city of the Bituriges and one of the finest in Gaul. It was, moreover, by nature very strong, being so protected by river and marsh that an en-

emy could not approach it save at one single point. This
the inhabitants had fortified with a wall forty feet thick
and made of great beams laid crosswise at intervals of
two feet and anchored on the inside. The spaces between
these were filled up with rubble, the face of which was
coated with huge stones. Thus the beams, buried as they
were, were impervious to fire. And by their strength the
wall was so held together that it could not be shaken
apart by battering rams.

Despite the promises of the people of Bourges to defend their city to the death, despite the strength of it and
the fact that it could not be blockaded, Vercingetorix
desired to have it burned. The council of chiefs was
against him, however, partly pitying the inhabitants of
Bourges and partly reckoning that it was easier and would
be less of a sacrifice to starve Caesar's army if it halted for
a while among the Bituriges. Vercingetorix gave way,
but he still refused a battle. He encamped sixteen miles
off and concentrated on attacking our foraging parties.
Caesar meanwhile came up to Bourges and started the
construction of a ramp with towers upon it which were
moved higher and nearer as his ramp increased in size.

The proper construction of siegeworks of this kind
had been new to the Gauls when Caesar had taken the
towns of the Belgians five summers ago. They had
thought it miraculous then, but now they were used to
it, and prepared with various desperate countermeasures.
They noosed Caesar's grappling hooks and hauled them
inside with windlasses. They undermined his ramp.
They built wooden towers on every part of their
wall, protecting them against fire with heavy hides.
They made sorties. Daily as Caesar's buildings grew
higher, they added stories to their own. They counter-

mined his mines or obstructed them with pointed beams and threw down boiling pitch or massive boulders.

All these measures took their toll, but Caesar's soldiers were mad to avenge the massacre of Orléans. In twenty-five days they had not starved or despaired, though they depended entirely on cattle driven in from remote farms too distant to have seemed worth burning. The common soldiers, who ate little meat as a rule, were sickened by it to the point where their stomachs could scarcely retain it. The work, however, went on despite the frost and the rain of that inclement spring. Already the ramp was eighty feet high and almost up to the wall.

It was midnight. Caesar as usual had not gone to bed, but was urging the soldiers on the night shift not to waste time. Someone called out to him that the ramp was smoking. There was a rush to the spot. The enemy had undermined it and set it on fire. Almost at the same moment a shout was raised on the wall, and the enemy sortied from two gates, one on either side of our towers. Those left on the wall began to throw torches and tinder and to pour down pitch on the ramp. All was in confusion.

Caesar had had the foresight to keep two legions on the spot bivouacking under arms. There were enough men on the work shift to draw the towers back, make a gap in the ramp to prevent it all burning, and start to put out the flames. Presently those asleep in the camp came up at the double.

Even so, the fight was long and hard. The protecting shields of our towers were burned out, as were some of our sheds, so that it was not easy to bring up reinforcements without cover. The enemy were fighting as though for the salvation of Gaul. Caesar noted one Gaul pitching lumps of grease and tow into the fire near one

of our towers from the town gate. A quick-firing catapult was trained on him, and he fell. The man next him
stepped over his body and carried on with his job. He,
too, was shot. A third succeeded him and to the third a
fourth. That post was manned until the ramp fire was
out and the fighting ended.

The sortie did us damage, but not more than we by
hard work could repair. Nothing now could prevent our
assaulting the city. Vercingetorix was adamant in refusing to sacrifice his army for the defense of Bourges.
He merely instructed the fighting men to get out across
the marshes and leave the town to its fate. But as they
prepared to steal away at night, the women and children
began to scream and wail. Fearing therefore that Caesar
would be warned by the noise and would send his cavalry to cut off the exits from the marsh, all stayed where
they were. Next day our structures were ready.

A heavy shower came on, which the Gauls apparently
expected to delay the assault. Caesar, however, had his
troops stripped for action under cover of the sheds, and
he gave the word. Dashing in through the downpour,
they gained the wall with little opposition. The enemy
tried to make a stand in the market place; but when they
perceived that our men were still filing onto the wall and
would not come down to level ground, they started to
panic. As they rightly suspected, Roman cavalry had
been sent out to surround the marsh. Many threw their
weapons down and made a rush for the farther end of the
town, where they jammed in the exits, which were narrow. Then the Romans waded into them, sword in hand,
and took their vengeance for Orléans, sparing neither
aged nor women and children, paying no attention to
booty in their dreadful lust for blood. Of forty thousand,

hardly eight hundred escaped. These had fled the town
at the first alarm and reached Vercingetorix, who did not
dare to let them into his camp in a single body. He feared
a mutiny against him and was forced to station his friends
along the road to intercept the wretches, sort them out,
and take them quietly to different sections of his camp.

Thus then fell Bourges. There had been murmuring
against Vercingetorix as long as the siege lasted, but
strangely enough the catastrophe increased his power.
He had been right, the Council wrong. The stocks of
food in Bourges delivered Caesar's army from present
danger of starvation. He could delay there until the
spring had advanced, for nothing further could be done
against the Aedui while he was present. Bourges ought
to have been burned.

All this being the case, none dared assail Vercingetorix's judgment. One or two chieftains had tried to attack
his motives. They had suggested he was secretly in
league with Caesar. This was preposterous, and Vercingetorix had treated it with fiery scorn. What could Caesar give him which the Gauls had not freely offered?
Was he not already a king and the leading man in Gaul?
He had not, however, assumed his great position to feed
his ambitions, but to be of service. Those who gave it to
him could have it back if they so pleased.

None pleased. Indeed, apart from Vercingetorix, they
had no plan for the war. His friends and envoys were
among the Aedui, in the very Province itself, among the
Germans and those few Belgian tribes who held to Caesar.
It was possible that a more general revolt might yet cut
the Romans off from every base and totally destroy them.

All these intrigues were not unknown to Caesar. The
key to his situation at present lay with the Aedui. Their

territories touched on the Province, which was his real base. They alone could afford him supplies in central Gaul. The Aedui, however, were rent with strife between the two great parties of those dead brothers, Diviciacus and Dumnorix. Indeed, they were almost on the verge of civil war. Their chief magistracy, an elective office, was claimed by two nobles at once. Such was their anarchy that the supplies which Caesar required were not forthcoming.

The victory at Bourges restored Roman prestige. Caesar was invited to arbitrate between the rival chiefs who claimed to rule the Aedui. Yet the very process of doing so plunged him in a dilemma. He was anxious above all to be fair, and yet the chief with the better right was the one whom he suspected of favoring the rebels. Was it possible that if the man owed his position to Caesar he would keep his tribesmen in line? There was no telling, but Caesar had to risk it. Injustice of any sort would certainly damage his reputation. He made the best of things by asking the Aedui for ten thousand infantry troops to add to his army. These with the Aeduan cavalry already in his camp might serve as hostages to keep their people loyal.

Meanwhile, however, initiative rested with Caesar. The grass was green enough for him to move, and there was much to be done. Determining to carry the war into his enemies' lands, Caesar split his army. Labienus with four legions marched north against the Parisians and their friends on the Seine. Caesar himself with six legions turned southwestward into Arvernian country and encamped in front of Gergovia. Vercingetorix, following as before without a pitched battle, occupied the lofty, sloping meadows south of the town.

Meanwhile, among the Aedui, the gratitude of their new magistrate to Caesar lasted only as long as the Romans lay at Bourges. As soon as the army marched away, his party feelings and the bribes offered by Vercingetorix overcame him. However, to induce the Aedui to revolt when many of their nobles were serving in Caesar's cavalry and when ten thousand infantry troops were about to set out to his aid did not seem easy. He therefore enlisted in this task the young commander of the ten thousand, a chief called Litaviccus, with whom he offered to share the rewards that Vercingetorix had promised.

Litaviccus accordingly marched out with his men and came within thirty miles of Gergovia. Here he paraded the whole ten thousand and tearfully told them that Caesar had put to death their cavalry chiefs, Viridomarus and Eporedorix, together with numbers of lesser people on the bare suspicion of treachery and without trial. He backed up his lie by bringing forward the men who were supposed to have brought him the news. Caesar had determined to massacre them all, and so Litaviccus offered to take them safely to the camp of Vercingetorix.

Viridomarus and Eporedorix were a pair of young chieftains, both tall and swaggering, with an insolent manner which served to conceal their shameless willingness to advance themselves by any possible means. They were as a matter of course bitter rivals secretly, though at present a partnership was to their advantage. Viridomarus had been a protégé of Diviciacus and was in consequence favored by Caesar. One might have imagined therefore that Eporedorix would have joined in Litaviccus's plot. When he heard of it, however, his only reaction was to steal a march on Viridomarus by betraying it to Caesar first. Accordingly, he slunk into Caesar's tent at midnight, the very picture of a secret conspirator, cloak over face and hand on sword.

I was in attendance on Caesar at this time, and I noted that when the Gaul had gone he sat still for minutes together and thought, the flickering glow from his stand of lamps picking out hollows in his cheeks and deepening the lines which ran from his nose to his mouth. Caesar looked older — as he might have looked had he lived fifteen more years. I remember the moment partly for this picture of him, but partly also because he sat so quietly. It was usual for Caesar to decide at once in a crisis what he should do. Indeed, the quickness of his judgment was in some ways the most remarkable thing about Caesar. He gave the impression of seeing all sides of a problem in a flash. Today, however, he brooded — and well he might do so. His position was awkward. Relying too confidently on his power to keep the Aedui in line, he had divided his army, sent Labienus to the north, and faced the unbeaten army of Vercingetorix with only six legions.

In Vercingetorix, Caesar had met a fit match at last. With disaffection spreading, the Roman needed a quick victory and could not get it. Thinking therefore to repeat the success of Bourges, he had come to Gergovia only to find it a very different nut to crack. Neither city could be surrounded and starved out. But whereas in one narrow section the approaches to Bourges had been easy, the mountainous slopes of Gergovia were impossible. Even on the southern side, the hostile army was encamped high up on its slope and protected from being charged uphill by a stone wall.

The weakness of Gergovia, as with all these mountain fastnesses, lay in its water supply. The townsfolk's cisterns could by no means suffice for a great army. The stream in the valley near which Caesar lay encamped went meandering past the bottom of Gergovia's slope for a long way, too far for six legions to hold it. Nevertheless, in the middle of Gergovia's south side, a very steep hillock rose suddenly out of the plain between the mountain and the stream. Caesar seized it and had hopes that he could in time still further constrict Vercingetorix's access to water. He posted two legions upon it; and because of his awkward position at the bottom of the hill he was forced to connect it to his main camp by a pair of wide, deep trenches, behind which his soldiers could go back and forth without being rushed.

Thus at the time of Litaviccus's plot Caesar's army was fully extended. It lay in two separate camps at the foot of a slope held by an enemy alert and, when he saw a chance, aggressive. If Caesar relinquished the siege of Gergovia to deal with the Aedui, the tidings would be spread all through Gaul as a Roman defeat. Incalculable would be the results. Labienus might be cut off and destroyed by a Belgian uprising. Even the Aedui in circumstances such as these would be hard to handle. Yet if Caesar did not march out with the bulk of his army at once he would lose the Aeduan ten thousand, and presumably too the Aeduan state, which would be deeply committed to Vercingetorix by their army. How then could Caesar retain the Aedui without abandoning Gergovia? Could he, for instance, evacuate the smaller camp? He would find it occupied by the enemy when he came back. Thereafter, all operations against Gergovia would be hopeless. Somehow or other he must march out in great strength and yet hold both his campsites.

No wonder Caesar brooded a while, for the risk he took

was tremendous. He left with four legions very quietly while it was yet dark, leaving two behind him to man the walls of the camp and pretend a normal bustle, though in fact it was unlikely that they could deceive the enemy for long. Caesar himself urged his men to make haste, notwithstanding the nature of the ground. He came up with the Aeduan contingent twenty-three miles away, marching to join Vercingetorix. He had with him Eporedorix and Viridomarus, whom they thought dead; and he easily convinced the Aeduan soldiers. Litaviccus and his personal retinue escaped to Vercingetorix. So far so good; but negotiations took time, and Caesar's troops were tired. He gave them three hours' rest. Then he started back, to be met by messengers from Fabius, to whom he had entrusted command of his two camps. The enemy were attacking in full force. Fabius was desperate. Caesar rode down the length of his legions, appealing to them. Our pace was quickened. No doubt in the darkness of that night's march a few men did fall out, but not many. To do so meant being killed and robbed before morning. Besides, centurions with sticks brought up the rear, driving the stragglers to stumble forward again. The army plunged on, glad of the cool night air, swaying with the rhythm of the march, hardly conscious that when it reached camp, if there still was a camp, it must fight.

This was our worst march of the war, very nearly fifty miles in twenty-four hours over broken country which is hardly ever flat for two hundred yards. Caesar had known what he could demand of his legions. The peril of the camps had been acute, yet they had survived. The Aeduan contingent and with it presumably the Aeduan state was with us once more. But on its lofty pinnacle still, Gergovia mocked us.

As it happened, news from Litaviccus had reached the
Aeduans before the messengers of Caesar. Riots broke
out straightway. Roman citizens were plundered and
attacked. For a night and a day the mob raged until it
was discovered that the soldiers were after all in Caesar's
power. At this, damage was hastily made good, while the
Aeduan government sent messengers to excuse itself to
Caesar. Secretly, however, they felt they had gone too
far, did not trust Caesar's pardon, and began to intrigue
with other tribes to join the revolt. The situation in Gaul
looked ominous indeed. Caesar had been too rash in di-
viding his army, in plunging hastily into the Arvernian
country, in attacking Gergovia. It would be wiser to retire from where he was without being forced. Yet before
he went, he needed a success of some sort which he could
trumpet as a victory. Appearances at this particular time
were all-important.

More or less to the east of Gergovia lay a mountain
called Risolles from which a neck of land gave access to
Gergovia itself. This was in fact the only place where
the approach to Gergovia was other than very steep,
though it was protected by the mountain of Risolles,
which must be climbed first. So far nobody had paid particular attention to this side of the town, which was at
the opposite end of the valley from Caesar's camp on the
southwest. It would be difficult for Caesar to maintain
himself where he was and to seize the mountain of
Risolles as well, but Vercingetorix had great respect for
his enemy's power to achieve the almost impossible. If
Caesar did manage to gain Risolles and dominate the neck,
Gallic water and forage would indeed be threatened. For
between Caesar's smaller camp and Risolles lay their
access to the stream. Accordingly, Vercingetorix deter-

mined to fortify the neck. For this purpose, Gallic entrenching instruments being primitive, he required vast
numbers of men. Thus Caesar, prospecting from the
smaller camp, found the southern slopes under Gergovia
which had been black with people almost empty.

It was not and never had been Caesar's intention to try
to take Risolles. The ground was difficult, and he did not
have sufficient strength. However, the comparative de-
sertion of the enemy's main encampment did tempt him
to try a raid in force on that. To be sure, it was twelve
hundred paces away in a straight line — and in order to
reach it one must zigzag because of the steepness of the
ground. It was also protected by a six-foot wall of stones,
no fearsome obstacle and yet not to be despised above
such a slope. Between this wall and the town of Gergovia
itself lay the Gallic encampment, half deserted as long as
the bulk of their force was at work on the neck. In order to keep it there, Caesar sent down the valley one
single legion and the pack horses and mules, mounted by
the camp servants wearing cavalry helmets to appear from
a distance like a formidable array. All these people were
to look as though they threatened Risolles.

While this was going on, Caesar's other legions were
moving in smallish, casual groups into his lesser camp,
which lay as I have mentioned at the foot of Gergovia's
slope opposite the middle of the long southern face of
the town. Here he instructed them in their business,
which was to rush the hill and storm the Gallic camp.
While they did so, the Aeduans in Caesar's larger camp
were to take a tortuous route which would eventually
bring them out on the southeast side of the hill, thus taking the Gauls in the flank.

Trumpets sounded. Two legions rushed out of our

camp, flung themselves at the steep hill, swarmed up
it, boosted each other over the wall, and were in the Gallic encampment long before any sort of line could be
formed against them. King Teutomarus of a tribe called
the Nitiobriges was taking a nap in his tent and only escaped us stripped to the waist and on a wounded horse.
Our men scattered to plunder and destroy and very
shortly in the confusion lost all semblance of battle order.
Meanwhile Caesar, who was following with the Tenth at
a slightly soberer pace, considered that enough had now
been done and sounded the recall.

What with the confusion and shouting of the Gauls,
what with the echoes in that place of hills and valleys,
Caesar's trumpets were not regarded. The two foremost legions had been strictly charged not to go too far,
but the ease of their penetration into the camp had fired
them. Loss of formation, too, meant loss of control.
Looming above them was the town of Gergovia itself.
Some of the women had rushed onto the walls to have
a look at the fight in the camp. With true Gallic temperament these were in a panic. Some were throwing clothes
or money down to our soldiers, begging for quarter.
Others even climbed down to give themselves up, prefer-
ring slavery to the horrors of a sack. Our men, em-
boldened, threw prudence to the winds and rushed for
Gergovia's wall.

Lucius Fabius, a centurion of the Eighth, was fired by
the memory of the prizes Caesar had distributed after
Bourges. He was determined to be the first on the walls
of Gergovia, and he found three men of his century to
boost him up. Gaining a foothold, he in turn hauled them
up beside him. A shout was thereupon raised that the
walls were won.

Meanwhile the Gauls from the neck came streaming into the battle, taking our men in the left flank. They were fresh. Our legions were winded. They outnumbered us. Our men fought with desperate courage, and soon the Aedui whom Caesar had sent up from his larger camp appeared on their right. This might have saved the day, but in the confusion the Romans did not know friend from foe. They mistook the Aedui for a fresh set of Gauls pressing in from the opposite direction. The legions wavered. Just at this moment, the centurion Fabius and his three friends were flung down dead from the wall. This incident proved the turning point, and our men fled.

The Gauls pursued in force, but Caesar checked them with the Tenth and with his reserves. Seven hundred Romans were lost, and, what was worse, nearly fifty centurions. Gallic losses must have been considerable too, but neither side took account of that. Gallic numbers by far exceeded ours, and their untrained levies were easily replaceable. One legionary soldier was worth a dozen Gauls or more, and both sides knew it.

For the first time, Caesar had overreached himself. He had not taken Gergovia, and he dared not stay to try. Instead of retreating with a victory to his credit, he had suffered defeat. Vercingetorix stood at the pinnacle of fame. He had shown how Caesar might be slowly foiled, worn down, just possibly destroyed if Gaul united. The Aedui and the Belgian tribes in the north would think this over.

5

This is the climax of the war, and once again the hero of it is not Caesar. Caesar's glory had long been assured. He could afford to take second place to Vercingetorix for one tragic moment. Once again, I have let the story speak for itself. My own personal struggles count as nothing beside those of Vercingetorix, Vercassivellaunus his cousin, even of Commius — though that resilient man was of no tragic stature. We fought as we had never fought before. Not even when beleaguered with Cicero had we expended ourselves so utterly. But in winning we perceived that the Gauls — or some of the Gauls — had excelled themselves likewise. They had put forth their supreme effort and lost. Death or slavery waited.

Viridomarus and Eporedorix came to Caesar as he retreated towards the Aeduan country. Litaviccus, who had so nearly brought over the Aeduan troops to Vercingetorix, had now gone back home with the tidings of Caesar's repulse. "It is essential," the two chiefs claimed, "that we go, too, and use our influence against him."

Caesar regarded them with a weary lack of enthusiasm. He was not disposed to trust any Aeduan at this stage of the war; yet if the tribe was going to revolt in any case, it probably mattered little what Viridomarus and Eporedorix did at this point. Besides, he had nothing against them and was anxious to act fairly with men who were loyal.

Viridomarus and Eporedorix therefore went ahead of the army with their own cavalry and came to Nevers on the Loire. Here Caesar was holding all the hostages he had received from the Gauls, his reserves of grain, public funds, his personal baggage, remounts for the cavalry, and stores in general. Nevers was not precisely an Aeduan town, but since it belonged to a dependent tribe it had been considered within their sphere of influence and safe for Caesar, who lacked at this time a secure base outside the Province.

Here at Nevers, Viridomarus and Eporedorix received news from the Aeduan capital of Bibracte. Litaviccus had been welcomed home by the chief magistrate and many of the nobles. Ambassadors had been sent to Vercingetorix to negotiate alliance. The two young chiefs from Caesar's camp found themselves not only powerless, but actually in danger from the rebel faction. It took them but a very short while to decide what to do. Nevers would be a present to the rebels of very great value. They were inside it with a considerable retinue of their own and trusted by the guards. It would be easy to cut down Caesar's men, to plunder the town, and to send Caesar's hostages to Bibracte. There they could be used to force their kinsmen to join with Vercingetorix. Meanwhile the two young chiefs would have earned their way back to favor.

It was indeed easy. Caesar's men were all murdered, his goods plundered, his grain loaded onto barges or thrown into the Loire, and Nevers itself burned to the ground, lest he retake it. With the supplies thus gained, Viridomarus and Eporedorix began to raise forces of their own and post detachments to try to prevent Caesar crossing the Loire, which at this season of spring was still in flood. If they could detain him between the Allier and Loire, they might starve him out.

While matters looked thus desperate for Caesar, the

Aeduans were using their position and the hostages they had unexpectedly gained to call a Council of Gaul at Bibracte. Almost all tribes attended. Vercingetorix was elected supreme commander. This by no means pleased the Aedui, who felt that their position gave them a right to take the lead. In especial, Viridomarus and Eporedorix after the taking of Nevers aspired to the post.

Vercingetorix outlined his plans, which were very much as before. He needed cavalry. His infantry sufficed, since he would not offer battle; but with cavalry in vastly superior numbers he could cut Caesar off from forage. For the rest, he intended to attack the Province on all sides, setting the Aedui to invade the Allobroges in the east, his own Arverni to fall on the Helvii in the center, and his southwestern allies to attack the Volcae in the west. Meanwhile, Vercingetorix had already secret envoys tampering with the loyalty of the Allobroges, who might just possibly revolt when they saw that Caesar could not help them.

While Caesar was thus trapped in central Gaul and while his base in the Province was threatened on all sides, Labienus in the country round the Seine was in trouble, too. He had ventured in pursuit of a Gallic force far down the Seine to Paris. In the meanwhile, news of the Aeduan revolt and Caesar's defeat at Gergovia had come north. The Bellovaci, who were a Belgian tribe north of the Seine, very warlike and so far not severely treated by Caesar, joined the revolt. To the north of these along the coast lay Commius at Boulogne, almost recovered from his wound. After the treachery of Volusenus, Commius had taken an oath that he would never save in battle look on a Roman again. His influence among the Bellovaci was strong, and in any case their present chance was a good one. Labienus by now was very anxious as to how he could get back to Sens. He had only four legions. The Bellovaci were behind him and a well-equipped Gallic army in front. His supplies and his baggage were cut off from his army by the Seine.

Thus it was that for a short interval the fate of Gaul hung in the balance. Vercingetorix was gathering contingents from the tribes. The tribes of the Province were assembling their forces, the Allobroges posting detachments along the Rhone, the Helvians under Dumnotaurus defending the country south of the Cévennes. Meanwhile Caesar was desperate for cavalry. Reinforcements from Italy or the Province would be blocked. The Gauls for the most part were no longer with him. The cavalry tactics of Vercingetorix presented a serious menace. Caesar communicated with the Germans, contracting to hire their cavalry and the special infantry which they trained to run with their horses. These men arrived very promptly, joining Caesar before the Aedui had time to collect a force and block their path. Their horses, which were nothing but little wild ponies, proved no use. Caesar's remounts had been taken at Nevers, so that he had nothing on which to mount his Germans but the horses he took from re-enlisted veterans, who traditionally have lighter duties and who ride on the march. These did not suffice, and he took our horses also. We younger officers had always owned our own and were permitted to have as many as we chose or could provide grooms for. I remember in especial a beautiful chestnut that I had to let go to that barbarian horde whose own poor creatures were shaggy, half starved, covered with welts, and brutally used. The times, however, were desperate. The German cavalry when properly disciplined and mounted could save us all.

Meanwhile, the Gauls fell on the Province. To the east and west they had little success, for the nature of the terrain and the disposition of the garrison towns was in our favor. In the center, however, the Arverni held the passes of the Cévennes, and they poured through them into the lands of the Helvii, where Gaius Valerius Dumnotaurus met them with the fighting forces of his tribe. I never knew Dumnotaurus personally, but I knew of him. There were rumors that he was almost an Arvernian himself, spent more of his time at Gergovia than he ever did at Vienne, and hated his brother Procillus, who was for so long the interpreter of Caesar.

Perhaps because much of this was true, Dumnotaurus was evidently burning to prove himself, both to the Helvians and to his father Caburus, Caesar's friend. He ought to have retired on the Helvian strongholds and let the enemy ravage his lands while he waited for help. Instead, outnumbered though he was, he gave battle. He was defeated and killed. I saw old Caburus years later at Vienne and wondered if people still remembered how he had been called a lucky man. His hands trembled. There were runnels at the corners of his eyes which looked as though they had been worn by tears. When I spoke to him of Procillus, whom I had loved, the drops went trickling down the side of his nose and splashed into his beard. Yet he sat with me far into the night talking of his sons.

While these events took place in the Province, Labienus burst through the armies encircling him, defeated the Gauls who stood in his way, and got back to Sens. Here he recovered his baggage and supplies, with which he marched to join Caesar, leaving the country behind him all in revolt. With four legions he was not strong enough to hold down the North now that the Bellovaci and Commius were active in the rising. Labienus knew also that Caesar would need him at once. The defeat of Gergovia must be erased, while the defection of the Aedui might cut off our army from the Province.

As a result of all these maneuvers, Caesar's army was feeling its way round the Aedui through the territory of the Sequani with the object of coming down from the rear on those who were attacking the Province. Vercingetorix meanwhile with about fifteen thousand horse and a large body of infantry still followed. "It is by no means part of my strategy to allow Caesar a safe retreat from Gaul," he pointed out to his council. "If he once penetrates to the Province, he will merely recoup his strength there and try again. Now is the moment to catch him while he is in flight." Despite his great abilities, Vercingetorix was a true Gaul, and the repulse from Gergovia had made him too sanguine. The Arvernians were displaying a sword which they boasted had been Caesar's own. Vercingetorix thought of our army as being by now in despair.

He still desired no pitched battle. Gallic levies, poorly armed and often not armored, went down like sheep before the legions; and he knew they always would. Only the chieftains and wealthy men in the first rank were formidable. Gallic cavalry was all made up of better-class men, rich enough to own their equipment. It was well armed, and it usually faced not the legions, but other Gauls fighting for Caesar. Our successes with this arm were simply and solely due to better discipline.

All these considerations had persuaded Vercingetorix

to keep the size of his army moderate as far as infantry went and to put his strength in the cavalry arm. He had with him many chiefs who had served in the past under Caesar and knew his methods. Vercingetorix had practiced his men, holding them back from major conflicts, but skirmishing day by day with Caesar's foragers and scouts. Very naturally when he perceived he must fight, what he thought of was a major cavalry exploit rather than a battle.

"My plan is to cut off Caesar's baggage train," he told them. "The legions will probably abandon it at once to save their skins. If they resist, then at least we shall delay them and add to their difficulties in reaching the Province. As for their cavalry, it is so far outnumbered that we can disregard it."

"We'll ride it down," the chiefs agreed.

"We'll ride straight through the Roman column."

"An oath! An oath!" one or two began to call, and the cry was taken up. Gauls are ready to bind themselves by oath in moments of excitement and are apt to make its conditions impossibly stringent to prove they mean what they say. On this occasion they bound themselves to ride twice through the enemies' column. He who failed to do so should never enter a house again or be allowed access to his children, wife, or parents. Such are the frenzied enthusiasms of Gauls.

The mistake Vercingetorix had made was that neither Caesar nor our army felt defeated or cast down. He was able to catch us by surprise because our scouting parties had been persistently driven in. There was, however, no question of our abandoning baggage. We simply formed a square about it, pushing our cavalry out to meet the enemy onslaught and using our legions as a screen behind which our horsemen could retreat when pressed. Thus, though the Gauls attacked on every side, they could not break us.

The battle was decided in the end by our German cavalry. In fact, the sacrifice of my favorite horse to them was far from in vain. Well mounted, well officered, they had become most formidable. They drove the Gauls before them down to the river, where Vercingetorix and his infantry awaited. At this, the rest of their cavalry were afraid of being taken in flank. They forgot their oath and fled. There was great slaughter, and several high chiefs were captured.

Thus was the defeat at Gergovia avenged. Now Vercingetorix must draw his army off. If he stayed where he was, his beaten cavalry could not prevent his being drawn into battle. He departed in much haste, and Caesar pursued him, neither army encumbering itself with its baggage train. Thus in reverse order they retired once more to the east, Caesar hoping to bring his enemy to bay, and Vercingetorix seeking for escape. After this fashion they came to the fated spot, the town of Alesia.

Alesia was a very similar fortress to Gergovia, and it was no doubt with similar intentions that Vercingetorix took refuge there. It too was lofty, somewhat oblong in shape, its longer sides to north and south bounded by narrow valleys, through which flowed a pair of parallel streams. On the east side between the streams another mountain arose. On the west side the land flattened out to a plain three miles long, through which meandered the river Brenne, which received the two tributary streams. As at Gergovia, every side of the hill of Alesia was very steep, while on it the Gauls lay encamped below the town, protected by a rough wall and a ditch. There was,

however, one single difference in the situation. In front
of Gergovia, Caesar had disposed of six legions. Here at
Alesia, he had ten. Even so, Caesar's lines of investment
must be over nine miles long with a ring of camps on the
outlying hills and twenty-three redoubts to guard against
surprise. There seemed some question whether with the
forces that he had, these lines could be held.

Vercingetorix did not permit himself to be walled in
without a struggle. Early in the proceedings, he sent his
cavalry down into the western plain. In spite of its recent
defeat, this still was greatly superior to ours in numbers
and threw our Gallic and Spanish horse back. The legions, however, once more provided shelter, while the
Germans again turned their success into rout. The
Gauls fled back to their camp, where they jammed in the
gateways, which were narrow. Our men, pursuing, began to cut them down. At that, there was panic in the
camp, and Vercingetorix was forced to shut the gates of
Alesia lest his men desert the slopes entirely and take refuge in the town. All hope of thrusting us out of the western plain by force was therefore over.

This is not to say that Vercingetorix was at this
moment besieged. Considering the circuit of our projected wall, this could hardly be. The fact was that to
move his army as a whole with its baggage train and all
its clumsy transport was now impractical because his cavalry was too demoralized to fend off pursuit. Yet the
cavalry itself could very easily slip away before our lines
were complete. Vercingetorix determined to dispense
with it before it was hemmed in on the slopes of the
mountain where it could be of no use. He sent it away
to gather aid. Let the Gauls come to his rescue while
Caesar's thin lines were fully extended. Let them crush

Caesar between Alesia and themselves. Then Gaul would be free.

The cavalry duly made its escape, while Vercingetorix organized his forces for a siege. The nominal owners of Alesia, a small, inoffensive tribe called the Mandubii, had driven in cattle from all their outlying farms, so that there was meat. There was also enough grain for thirty days. Vercingetorix collected all under his central control and doled out rations.

While all this was going on, and while the chieftains of Gaul were deliberating the rescue of Vercingetorix, Caesar's army dug. We dug for dear life, night and day in shifts, our only respite from the monotonous work being our expeditions for timber, food, and forage. Caesar intended to provision his army for thirty days and to stand siege himself if he must, for this time he had his grip on Alesia and would never let go.

Our first project was a trench twenty feet wide and with perpendicular walls which we dug at the western end between the two parallel rivers to cut the garrison off from the plain. This ditch was not manned and merely served to allow us to concentrate troops against a sudden rush. Four hundred yards behind on the plain our main works lay . . . first a trench fifteen feet wide and eight deep. This also extended from river to river across the western end. Behind it came another trench of similar dimensions, this extending round the nine-mile circuit of the town and filled with water from the streams wherever the level of the land was sufficiently low. Behind this came a rampart and palisade twelve feet high, further protected by stout forked branches which projected downward and made it difficult to climb. Around the whole circuit we built towers at intervals of eighty feet.

Not even yet was Caesar satisfied, since the garrison of Alesia, knowing that our forces were stretched thin, was making mass sorties which were scarcely beaten back. He now dug ditches five feet deep inside his moat into which he fixed tree trunks with their branches still on, all sharpened to a point. In front of these again were sharp-pointed stakes embedded in small pits concealed by brush-wood. Finally he had barbed spikes fixed in pieces of wood which had been sunk in the ground. Thus protected, he turned his attention to outer works of a similar sort against the relieving force which he expected.

Meanwhile, the Council of Gaul assembled at Bibracte was discussing the relief of Alesia at its leisure. There were all sorts of local jealousies to be resolved in the fascinating business of fixing a contingent for each tribe. The relief of Alesia was to be an all-Gallic task in which even the remote tribes on the ocean must be given their fair share. No doubt the Aedui, who were jealous of Vercingetorix, were not particularly anxious to rush to his rescue too soon. It suited them that the tribes should slowly gather while Caesar built his walls and Alesia hungered. This was not, however, the view of the tribes as a whole. Forty-three of them were summoned, and from all save the Bellovaci horse and foot came pouring in. The Bellovaci, though for some time in rebellion, would not send. They would fight Caesar in their own place and their own way. They were a free people and had no intention of submitting to other folks' orders. Eventually they consented to supply a token force, purely in compliment to Commius, who was their northern neighbor and had great influence among their tribe.

Who can count a Gallic army? We never saw this one deployed as a whole because of the nature of the ground.

Their estimate of it themselves is that their foot were a quarter of a million and their cavalry eight thousand. It is certain that of all the armies Caesar faced, this one in especial has a right to be considered the army of Gaul.

Not that this was a source of strength to them. It might have been so, had Vercingetorix directed it. But Vercingetorix was no more to them than their totem, their sacred standard, almost their Eagle. They died for him, but other men assumed command. First of these were Viridomarus and Eporedorix, the Aeduan leaders, still rivals, prepared to concede no inch to each other. With them Commius was joined. At the moment Commius was riding on a wave of popularity because he had escaped being murdered. The scar of his great wound and his oath to meet no Roman marked him for a national hero. To these three commanders Vercassivellaunus, an Arvernian and cousin to Vercingetorix, was added. One may say of him that he cared less for himself and more for the cause than did the others, though in the end it availed him very little.

With four generals-in-chief, the Gallic army might have seemed rather overcommanded; but of course there had to be a council as well. Even Vercingetorix had not been free of this encumbrance. With forty-three tribes, the council was large and more obstreperous than ever. Both it and the army were full of good spirits and hope. They had caught Caesar at last, and no experience persuaded them he was a dangerous man to corner.

Meanwhile, the besieged had waited thirty days, for which they had adequate rations. Then with starvation staring them in the face, they waited twenty more. Still the army which was to destroy Caesar had not arrived. Their council assembled and deliberated what to do.

Some were for surrender, others for a sortie while they still had their strength. One chief reminded them that when driven into their strongholds by the Cimbri and the Teutons years before, they had eaten each other. None were ready for this desperate expedient yet, but the one they resolved on was almost as cruel. All noncombatants, be they women or children or aged folk, must leave the town. Accordingly the Mandubii, who were the inhabitants of the place, were driven out ruthlessly to go and beg mercy from Caesar's lines. Unhappily Caesar was desperate, too. Well he knew that his fate and that of his army hung in the balance. He could not afford to relax his pressure for an instant. The wretched Mandubii wandered back and forth between the lines in despair and found pity nowhere.

Most luckily at this time the army arrived. Those in Alesia saw its cavalry moving into the plain, while its main army lay encamped on a hill to the southwest a mile from Caesar's entrenchments. A fierce cavalry combat took place in full view of the three armies. Caesar posted his men on both his lines. Those in Alesia brought hurdles and earth to fill up the first trench and held themselves ready to assault. The relieving army stayed in its encampment, waiting the issue of the cavalry battle.

This was for many hours in doubt. The Gauls had mingled archers and light-armed infantry with their horsemen. These were unexpected and did great execution. Naturally also they had the advantage in numbers. Their waiting armies, both on the slopes of Alesia and on the hill outside, cheered on their men. Ours, too, were encouraged by our shouts and fought as though possessed. Not till almost sunset when both sides were equally weary did Caesar bring out his best troops. Then the victorious Germans, charging like a thunderbolt, broke up the exhausted Gauls. They fled. The archers were exposed and killed. Our men pursued them up to their camp, while those in Alesia retreated gloomily back into the town.

Next day all was quiet. The relieving army was preparing scaling ladders, grappling hooks, and bundles of brush to fill up the ditches. Round about midnight they stole very silently out of their camp, then raised a tremendous shout to summon Vercingetorix as they dashed at our ditches. Thence they began to pelt our men on the ramparts with slingshots, arrows, and stones. None of our people were far from their stations, even at night, so that in a minute our slingshots were whizzing into their dark mass, supports were hurrying up from the neighboring redoubts, quick-firing catapults were creaking as they were wound and whirring angrily as they let their javelins go.

There was wild shouting from all sides. It was especially nerve-racking to hear the enemy behind us. Our lines crossing the plain were not far apart, so that Vercingetorix and his men seemed right on our rear, notwithstanding the three ditches, the iron hooks, the sharpened stakes, and the other rampart. Meanwhile, the enemy who were actually our concern had fallen into trouble. As long as they stood at the outer ditch, their stones and missiles made it difficult for our men to man the ramparts. When, however, they started to advance, they fell in the darkness into our various traps, for which they were not prepared. Now there was great confusion among them, with noise of men screaming as well as yelling. As the number of their missiles diminished, ours increased, since we were no longer pinned down.

This fierce, confusing struggle went on till nearly dawn, and the casualties of the Gauls were extremely heavy. Vercingetorix, however, had far more trouble to fill our ditches up, since there were three on that side instead of one. His people had improved their time in making movable shelters for their attacking troops. These were hard to get over the ground. For all these reasons, they had scarcely reached our defenses when the outer assault was broken off. Thus they retreated likewise with nothing accomplished.

Twice repulsed in headlong assault, the Gauls now took the trouble to reconnoiter the ground on every side. Caesar's inner works, as I have said, were nine miles long. They followed everywhere the streams and the level ground to prevent the garrison of Alesia from assaulting from above. The outer works, which ran very close to the inner across the plain itself, were elsewhere farther apart, so that the whole circuit of them was nearly twelve miles. Caesar had drawn them across low-lying hills in such a fashion that the ground sloped away from them and those assaulting would have to charge uphill. Only at one point was he unable to do this. North of the western plain rose a mountain called Rea, too big to encircle, and yet separated from Alesia by such a narrow valley that two defensive lines could not be drawn in it. Accordingly, Caesar traced his outer line on the slope of Rea, accepting because he must the fact that doing so would allow the Gauls to attack from higher ground. In the hope of protecting this weak spot, he had established a camp for two legions very near by.

The Gallic generals laid their plans. Vercassivellaunus with a large force of picked men stole out of their camp in the darkness, crossed the plain, and marched round

Mount Rea, reaching by morning a point somewhere to the northeast whence the ground led easily to that slope which was the weakest point of Caesar's lines. Here they rested for a while and by noon felt themselves ready to move on to the attack. At this time, by prearrangement, the cavalry streamed onto the plain, while the infantry of the main body descended to the scene of their previous defeat. Vercingetorix, perceiving that a move was to be made, descended also.

This time there was little delay at the inner trenches. Parts of these had been leveled already, and Caesar could not now spare the men to dig them out. The roar of battle rose on all sides in the plain. Vercassivellaunus and his men, taking advantage of their higher ground, bombarded our men with dreadful effect from Mount Rea. The hail of their weapons not only did great damage, but by forcing our soldiers to shelter themselves with extreme care, it interfered with their return volleys. Profiting from this, the Gauls were able to fill up our ditch and pile earth over our mantraps. Then, interlocking their shields above their heads, they rushed to the assault with grappling hooks to pull down our ramparts and breastwork.

Caesar had found himself a spot to the south of both battles, where a rising slope gave him a view across the plain and onto the side of Mount Rea. He had with him his secretaries — freed slaves — and a group of officers who, being mounted men, might serve as his messengers. He was mounted himself and sat there almost unmoving while a groom stood quietly by his horse's head. He had given his helmet to his attendant to hold, and the wind ruffled his sparse hair. His aquiline profile was turned to us as he looked at the battle, now and then biting at his underlip, as was his way when excited. Every so often he would point and turn to his nearest aide, "See that!" or "What do you think?" Woe betide the officer who had not his answer pat. Caesar loathed hesitation.

He was bringing up reserves at the double and throwing them in at each threatened spot. These, however, must be taken from somewhere else round our vast circuit, nearly all of which was out of sight, while much was out of hearing. It was not impossible that still another assault might be made elsewhere. The Gauls had sufficient men to pin ours down, even though the advantage of terrain was with us all around the western end. For this reason the farthest parts from the battle were lightly manned, and our main infantry camps were north and south. Still, two or three miles must often be traversed, and it behooved Caesar to know not where need lay, but where it *would* lie. Meanwhile he was gathering reserves from wherever he could and massing them near him, while edging soldiers back and forth on the actual ramparts.

All this called for a keen eye, an iron nerve, and a marvelous memory for detail. The exact numbers of men in every position, the probable casualties, the location of every catapult, almost of every centurion, must be reckoned. Where our numbers were so sparse, exact economy of men and means would alone decide the issue.

Fortunately the attack in the plain was not so serious as that earlier made. Vercassivellaunus had drained off the picked men, while the average peasant who forms the chief part of a Gallic array has neither good weapons nor the desire to expose himself without them. Besides, Vercassivellaunus had the rescue of his cousin at heart, while the Aeduan chieftains were opportunists who had once deserted Caesar and who, if things went awry, might serve him again. For all these reasons, the attack on the south-

west side was not too seriously pressed, while Vercingetorix, coming up for the first time against our actual rampart, found it so strong that he diverted his forces to an
easier sector and lost time. Had it not been so, great as
our defenses were on the plain, they must have been lost.
Vercassivellaunus had drawn most of our reinforcements
to him. Caesar sent Labienus thither with strict instructions to hold the sector if he could, if not to fight his way
out. While the issue of this struggle still hung in the balance, Caesar rode down into the plain to show himself
there and to urge all he met to hold on somehow. On this
hour their future and the success of all their past efforts
hung.

We did hold on. The failure of Vercingetorix to
breach the inside wall and the halfheartedness of those
without became apparent. Labienus sent back a message
that he had gathered a legion, or its equivalent in bits and
pieces, and wished to try a charge. Caesar therefore withdrew four cohorts from the plain, where fighting had begun to die away. He ordered half the cavalry to follow
him and half to circle the entrenchments and take Vercassivellaunus in the rear. Thus he proceeded to join
Labienus at the point of attack.

The enemy on both sides saw him come, for there were
many swarming on the hills on either side who could see
Caesar advance across the plain in his scarlet cloak with
the cavalry squadrons and the infantry cohorts following
behind him. With a tremendous shout, they made a last
effort; but already those who desired to fight were far
outnumbered by those who preferred to hang back. Un-
supported, Vercassivellaunus and his best men recoiled
for a moment. Labienus charged.

Caesar arrived at the spot to see the combatants retiring

over the slopes of Mount Rea. Just then the cavalry
whom he had sent on ahead caught them from behind.
With one of those instant changes which are characteris-
tic of Gauls, all was in panic. Men fled, and the cavalry
pursued. Vercassivellaunus himself was captured, and
seventy-four Gallic standards. His utter rout was visible
from Alesia, and Vercingetorix retired. All night the cavalry hunted men down and slew, for the main army of
the Gauls was too panic-stricken to stay in the safety of
their encampment. In their disorderly fashion they fled
and would not have escaped without utter disaster, save
that we were all too wearied for pursuit.

Next day Vercingetorix summoned his council. All
was lost, and he would so far as he could take the conse-
quences on himself. He had not chosen to lead the Gauls
in revolt for his own ends, but for their sake. Now they
might either kill him or sell him to Caesar in return for
their lives. He was in their hands.

Better far would it have been had they killed him
then, but they did not. They sent to Caesar and made
what terms they could. He was by no means in a forgiving mood. Gaul needed a lesson, and his own soldiers
neded plunder. For to Caesar's far-seeing gaze the faint,
unwelcome prospect of a fight to the death with Pompey
for Rome had come into view. The devotion of his soldiers to their paymaster might yet mean far more than
the conquest of Gaul.

Caesar told the Gauls to surrender their chief persons
and lay down their arms. It was his intention to spare the
Aedui and the Arverni, whose friendship he needed.
From the rest of the tribesmen, he would give each soldier one to sell as a slave. As for Vercingetorix, he would
march in Caesar's triumph at Rome, where his handsome

appearance and gorgeous arms would be duly admired.
That evening he would be put to death, for such is our
custom, and such it always has been since the birth of our
city.

There thus remained two ceremonies, Vercingetorix's
surrender and Caesar's triumph. I saw them both, and
of the two, the first moved me more. He came riding
down the slope from Alesia in all his splendor, the handsomest, richest, most glorious chieftain in Gaul. His
great black horse must have been groomed for the last
time by loving hands, for it shone like glossy silk, though
the ribs showed through its hide. His bronze helmet
also shone, with its crest like the wild boar. His oval
shield was not the one he had fought with, for it was un-
dented, save where it was engraved with spiral patterns,
the like of which I never saw before. His cloak was gold
and green, and all his ornaments and those of his horse
trappings were gold. He had his great sword by his side
and carried his spear.

After this fashion, Vercingetorix rode down the slope
from Alesia all alone, for the other chiefs reined back,
while those of his countrymen who had begun to stream
out of the town opened ranks as for a review. Caesar also
had given some thought to this ceremony. He had seated
himself on a makeshift chair of state on a little knoll, bareheaded, but in his armor and scarlet cloak with the Eagles
behind him. As Vercingetorix approached, we eyed him
in uneasy fashion, not liking his weapons, yet wishing to
make no move till Caesar desired it. Caesar looked stonily
ahead. Either he was angry that his prisoner should thus
presume, or else he was wearing his customary cold look
in anticipation of the scenes which follow surrender.

Vercingetorix picked his way slowly down the slope,

and then as the ground flattened out he quickened his
pace, raising his spear, not in a menacing gesture, but with
a wild flourish as though he would savor to the end the
joy of living. After all, he was very young. So he came
clattering down upon Caesar, while all we attendants
looked to our weapons in case he dared to die fighting.
He must have known, however, that if he did so he would
bring death on his people. He merely circled Caesar's
mound while both armies watched. Then reining up his
horse, he leaped to the ground.

Here he began to take off his armor and his ornaments,
piling beside him his bracelets, his gold torque, his cloak
and great round brooch. Now we could see him as he
had become — gaunt and haggard, with the high color
and the look of eagerness gone. Little of his beauty remained, save the red hair blazing in the sun. He knelt at
Caesar's feet.

They took him away and chained him. What else had
he to expect? I saw him for the last time at Caesar's triumph. That, however, was Caesar's day. Vercingetorix,
all shrunken and white from his years in an underground
dungeon, could scarcely bear the weight of all these trappings he had put off with pride. Even his hair by now had
lost its color, as red hair does when it turns dirty gray.
Neither Caesar nor he on that day of surrender can have
seen how long his misery would stretch out. For Gallic war gave place to civil war, and Caesar fighting in
every quarter of the known earth had little leisure to in-
quire how a prisoner did or arrange a procession. Six
years Vercingetorix dragged out in his dungeon and was
granted the release of death on the evening of that triumph. He must have been glad of it, and yet I suppose
that he was not yet thirty.

6

AFTERMATH

We were all aware the Gallic war was over. Caesar had gained equality in reputation and power with Pompey, and in consequence civil war loomed. Quintus Cicero heard much of political maneuvers against Caesar in Rome from his great brother. He imparted them to to us with small discretion. As a consequence we fought a scrappy war with brigands, looking dubiously the while at Rome and Caesar. Little Varus and his like were Caesar's to the death. So were the centurions. We officers came from political families in Rome, and we would choose. In consequence of this, the final agony of Lucterius and Drappes at Uxellodunum was an irritation to us, a dragging on of something with which our thoughts had finished. Even Commius, whom once we had considered the blackest traitor of all, had become a mere nuisance. We let him fight out his feud with Volusenus and escape. We did not care. Gaul was completely ours, but far more terrible and bitter wars lay ahead — for all save me.

THIS WAS the real end of the Gallic war, not the last of the fighting, but the last of the free chiefs of Long-haired Gaul. When Vercingetorix came riding down from Alesia, burnished like the sun, he gave us a final glimpse of their untamed pride. Then he vanished, none knew to what living death, and left no other. We fought brigands. We harried desperate men and sullen men, while the chiefs of the Arverni and of the Aedui intrigued once more for Caesar's favor. Caesar wintered in Bibracte with his army disposed about him. In January he was out in the field with two legions, harrying the Bituriges in spite of the weather.

I was myself on the Saône under Quintus Cicero, who was superintending the shipment upriver of grain from the Aeduan country and from the Allobroges in the Province. Here news came to us in February that Caesar was again in Bibracte after compelling the submission of the Bituriges, and that he had sent his legions back to winter quarters. We were told, moreover, that he had promised a bonus of two hundred sesterces to every private soldier and two thousand to each centurion because of the winter campaign. We were all envious of the Eleventh and Thirteenth, and I remember discussing what the officers would get. Serving as they did officially at their own cost, it would not have been proper for Caesar to proclaim a bonus to them. He would, however, be generous without a doubt. Quintus Cicero, who was our political expert on account of his constant letters from his brother in Rome, supported this view.

"It's the beginning," he remarked, pursing his lips and nodding wisely. "You mark my words, it'll be our turn next — or if not next, then soon. This winter campaigning's a mere excuse. Caesar's buying our allegiance."

We did not pretend to misunderstand, but some of us appeared surprised. Away from Rome, one gets quite out of touch, relying on casual letters for news. And of course Gallic affairs had been absorbing. Besides, in his desire to show off his knowledge, Quintus Cicero was being indiscreet.

"You mean," young Marcellus asked cautiously, "that Caesar already looks forward to the date of laying down his command? That's two years from now."

"Just so," Quintus Cicero agreed. "And what happens then?"

"He stands for the consulship," I put in, a little anxious lest the conversation turn awkward. "It'll be ten years since he had it."

"Oh yes, he stands." Quintus Cicero would not be put off. "But how does he do it? Can he go to Rome as a pri-

vate citizen in 49 and stand for election? His command
here expires on the first of March. We used to imagine
he'd retain it till the end of the year because a substitute
could not be sent out sooner. Pompey's law last summer
altered that."

"It made an exception of Caesar," Marcellus said without conviction.

Cicero laughed. None of us laughed with him. We
knew the law of Pompey was aimed at getting Caesar out
of his province at the earliest legal moment. We knew
also that if Caesar appeared in Rome as a private man, he
was lost. His many enemies would trump up charges
against him, either because of what he had done in his
province, or on account of some act of his consulship
which they chose to consider illegal. He would be con-
victed by a packed jury, exiled or put to death — at all
events ruined. Caesar's safety lay in being proconsul in
Gaul till the end of December, 49, and consul in Rome
the next day. We all knew this; but there was an un-
spoken opinion among us that the subject was better
avoided.

"That's two years away," I said shrugging. "Two
years is an age!"

Cicero laughed again at my ignorance. "Two years!
Dare Caesar wait till the day he's stripped of his command? He'll have to take action the moment the Senate
tries to appoint his successor for March of 49. That's why
he's buying the legions' support as fast as he can. I tell
you, our turn's coming."

This time nobody said anything. I suppose that none
of us had thought the matter through so far. I stole a
side glance at Marcellus. This year his uncle was consul
and was known to be an enemy of Caesar's. We were on

a subject far better not discussed with Marcellus at all. One never knew who might live to regret such a conversation.

The topic was dropped, but after that in another sense the Gallic War was over. None of us was old enough to have known the last civil war, save Quintus himself, but every one of us could have listed relatives lost in the wholesale murders which followed that conflagration. We saw ourselves drifting into a future we feared. People seemed to group themselves in a new way. For instance I drew apart from Marcellus, though I had liked him. I was starting to wonder what Marcellus reported to Rome about us all.

As concerned the immediate future, Cicero was right. Scarcely ten days later, Caesar called us out of winter quarters to help in a campaign against the Carnutes all around Orléans. Mopping-up expeditions are always dreary affairs, and this was certainly the worst I ever took part in. It was very early March, and the weather was frightful. We took up headquarters in Orléans, simply turning the Gauls out of the rude houses they had reconstructed in the place, or building huts over our tents with turf and thatch. From there we ravaged far and wide, driving the people out of their miserable homes to perish in the snow while we returned to camp laden with their belongings. Eventually, when most of the destitute wretches had fled as best they could to neighboring tribes, Caesar left us in Orléans to keep order in the desert he had made, while he turned his attention to his old friend Commius, who with the Bellovaci was in arms.

Undaunted by his defeat at Alesia, Commius had managed to assemble another huge army from the Bellovaci and various neighboring tribes, including his own. When

Caesar arrived, Commius had gone off to get help from the Germans, evidently trusting that the persuasiveness which never failed him would induce those barbarians to venture just once more across the Rhine.

Caesar found the Bellovaci in a typical position on a hill in a wood protected by a marsh. Hearing from captives that they had resolved to give battle if he brought no more than three legions, he made an effort to disguise the four he had with him as merely three. Whether he was unsuccessful, or whether the nerve of the Bellovaci failed them, the Gauls stayed where they were in a very strong position and contented themselves with harassing our foraging parties.

Caesar soon perceived that he had not men enough with him. The size of the Gallic host was vast, and since it was active against his foragers, he found it difficult to spare enough men for these expeditions without dangerously denuding his camp. Accordingly, he sent for three more legions, including our two at Orléans. Meanwhile he fortified his position by a double ditch and a rampart and breastwork, on top of which he erected three-story towers, connected with each other by covered bridges. Thus the bridges protected the men on the ramparts from falling missiles, while the men on the bridges were far above the enemies' heads and could throw farther.

While this was going on, the Bellovaci had some success against our cavalry which made them very conceited of their prowess. Moreover, Commius returned to camp with five hundred German horsemen — the merest token force, but one which his genius managed to represent as earnest of great things to come. Daily cavalry battles took place in front of both camps at the crossing places of the marsh, in which now one side was successful, now the other.

After a wait of some time in which nothing more occurred, our extra legions from Orléans were known to be approaching. The Bellovaci in the usual barbaric fashion had assembled not only their adult men, armed or unarmed, but their women and children and aged, who had otherwise no protection. Their unwieldy host was growing short of provisions, and since they had with them vast numbers of draft animals, their forage problem was incomparably greater than ours. Thus passing rapidly in the way barbarians do from extreme insolence to confusion in the face of difficulties, they resolved on retreat. This made it necessary for them to send their baggage on ahead. But swollen as it was with their noncombatants and household gear, they were forced to consume the whole night in getting it started. When dawn broke, the last of it was still plodding off, and the Bellovaci drew up their armed forces in front of their camp to prevent a Roman pursuit.

Caesar was far from unwilling to let the baggage train go and fight a battle. However, even with his reinforced strength he was reluctant to expose his legions as they struggled through the marsh. He therefore crossed it not opposite the Gallic line, but on its flank, where he could reach a plateau which was separated from their hill by a narrow depression. This brought him into such a threatening position that though by now the baggage train was well under way, the Bellovaci dared not follow. Once they broke up their line, the tribal contingents would as usual become confused, and the Roman cavalry would be on them in a trice. The Bellovaci stayed grimly under

arms, though all their provisions had been sent on ahead
with the baggage. Finally, near nightfall we saw them
bringing forward great bundles of straw and sticks which
they laid in front of their line and set ablaze.

In a matter of moments a wall of smoke and flame hid
the Gauls from our sight. Thereupon they all individually
turned their backs and fled away. Caesar attempted to
follow, but he was obliged to act with caution because he
could not see what they had done. Our horses, moreover,
were afraid to plunge into the fire. The few that did so
were blinded and choked by the smoke and forced to return. After this, the enemy took up another strong position ten miles off on the bank of the Oise.

These inconclusive maneuvers were brought to an end
by the Bellovacan leader. As Caesar learned from a captive, he planned to lay an ambush for our foragers in a flat
meadow to which he felt sure they must come. The place
was surrounded by woods and a deep river. Accordingly
the Bellovaci moved six thousand of their best infantry
and a thousand cavalry to ambush the position, fully ex-
pecting that our men, taken by surprise, would be prevented from escaping by the nature of the ground.

Unfortunately for the Gauls, our cavalry was not surprised. It had been sent out in considerable strength to
spring the trap with the light infantry close behind and
the legions to follow. Thus, though confused from the
first shock, it rallied and began to fight back, being
quickly supported by the light infantry. Hard fighting
followed, and both sides were still confident of victory
when the approach of the legions was announced. The
enemy lost heart at this and fled in every direction. Here,
however, they were caught in their own net, for the woods

and the river blocked them off from escape, and most were slaughtered.

This defeat, though by no means fatal to their numbers, took all the heart out of the Bellovaci. Once the picked people of a tribe are destroyed, there is no strength in the horde. Before Caesar could so much as approach their camp, which was eight miles off, they had sent ambassadors to treat for a surrender. Commius, seeing that the game was up, had fled to the Germans, doubtless still hoping that he could persuade them to renew the war.

Thus dissolved the last Belgian army. Caesar divided his army again, sending us towards Brittany and southwestern Gaul, while he took his own forces once more into the land of the Eburones. This wretched people had done nothing fresh to offend him, save to straggle back in diminished numbers to their wrecked homes and try to rebuild them. But Ambiorix was known to be hiding in their hills; and Caesar had determined that if he could not capture their chief, he would take his vengeance once more in the blood of that people. He desired them to hate Ambiorix for the fate he had brought upon them.

This raid was the same as the last — burned cottages, swollen corpses, miserable plunder, rain, despair, and hatred. I was glad I did not see it. I was marching with the Legate Fabius to a place called Poitiers, where the Picts and the Andes were besieging a loyal chief with a force of many thousands.

We disposed of the Picts with little trouble in the course of two cavalry actions. Even the most sanguine Gaul saw that we were invincible now. It had been possible to raise a rebellion among these western tribes because the war so far had spared them. It was one thing, however,

to call men together, and another to get them to fight. Like
the Bellovaci, the Picts and their neighbors promptly collapsed. We took their hostages and marched on to the
south, where two desperadoes still hopelessly in arms
were threatening the Province.

I call these men desperadoes because they had not even
the support of their own tribes and lived as brigands. One
of them was indeed a man of these parts, Lucterius, friend
and neighbor of Vercingetorix, who had sent him to win
the southwestern tribes and attack the Province. During
the previous year he had made a name for himself as a
very daring leader. Thus when Vercingetorix surrendered and the revolt collapsed, all sorts of outlaws who
feared the vengeance of Caesar fled to Lucterius. He was
about this time joined by another chief of a similar sort,
one Drappes, who had infested the country of the Senones
and immobilized our men for a while at Sens by cutting
off supply convoys. As all the country of northern and
central Gaul was now overrun, Drappes had drifted south
with about two thousand exiles, freed slaves, criminals,
and other riffraff which the dislocation of a great war had
produced. These two kindred spirits had now joined
hands and were planning to refit and recoup their supplies
by a raid on the Province.

Unhappily for them, we were hard on their heels. Caninius Rebilus had left us to deal with the ocean tribes
while he marched on Lucterius and Drappes with two
legions. Not daring to raid the Province with an army at
their back, the chiefs decided to seize as their base Uxellodunum, which was among the original dependencies of
Lucterius in prosperous times.

Caninius arrived in front of Uxellodunum, which
though smaller was even more precipitous than Gergovia

had been. However, the circle of the hill was not very great, and he decided to begin a fortification as far as his forces permitted.

Drappes and Lucterius beheld his preparations with dismay. They remembered Alesia. They were, however, pinned down in Uxellodunum very much after the fashion that Vercingetorix had been. They could certainly escape from the town at present; but to do so they would have to abandon their baggage, without which they could scarcely survive, since the country was hostile. A better alternative, they thought, would be to leave a garrison in the place while they themselves stole out with their light-armed troops to collect provisions which they could introduce before Caninius was strong enough to prevent them.

This therefore they did, and were generally successful in gathering tribute from the neighboring Cadurci, partly because Lucterius was secretly still popular with many, partly because the demands of two thousand men in a hurry are not to be resisted. Consequently in a very short while Drappes and Lucterius were back ten miles from Uxellodunum, planning to introduce into the town the grain they had gathered.

This they decided to do little by little. Drappes remained to guard their camp, while Lucterius attempted to take a mule train of supplies into the city. By now, however, the approaches were well guarded. Our Roman sentries heard the noise and sent out scouts. The provision bearers fell into a panic, while the armed men with them were not sufficient in numbers to repulse ours. Nearly all were cut down, and though Lucterius escaped with a few men, he was not successful in getting back to the camp where Drappes lay.

Caninius guessed this from the direction of Lucterius's flight, and he made his prisoners give details as to exactly where Drappes lay encamped. Setting out in that direction before the tidings of Lucterius's defeat could arrive, he burst into the place and destroyed it also. Drappes was taken alive. It is typical of the spirit of these desperate men that he starved himself to death within a short time.

Caesar meanwhile had joined us among the Carnutes, where he was administering justice and where the news of what went on around Uxellodunum was rapidly brought to him.

Caesar determined to go to Uxellodunum himself and to take it. The size of the citadel and the number of men in arms were not very great. Provisions, however, were said to be ample now that Lucterius and Drappes with their forces had left the town. Caesar judged it important that no example of successful defiance encourage Gaul. If Uxellodunum held out all summer, and if the weather forced him to abandon the siege in the end, then next year also he would have to stamp out revolts and march his legions the length and breadth of Gaul. Warfare would spring up wherever he turned his back. The following summer was Caesar's last in Gaul, and he intended to use it in demonstrating to the beaten tribes that Roman rule was better than their own. For he knew that he might need the legions elsewhere, and he was anxious that the war should as soon as possible be over in Gaul.

Caesar came to Uxellodunum, therefore, and examined the place. As Caninius had told him, it was impregnable. Not only were the sides of the hill too precipitous for siegeworks, but it was also surrounded by a river in the valley as though by a natural moat. To this river the townsfolk could come with impunity and bring their animals to drink, for the slope of the ground was so steep that Caesar could not easily establish himself across it.

Perceiving that he could neither storm the place nor starve it out, Caesar decided that he must deny the inhabitants access to water. He would have diverted the stream, but since it already flowed through the lowest part of the valley, he could not do so. However, the precipitous hill made the descent of the townsfolk and their ascent again necessarily slow. Caesar posted his catapults, his archers and slingers all round the bank of the stream. It rapidly became almost impossible for the enemy to get down to the water and hopeless to try and get back. Day and night our keen-eyed watchmen guarded the bank.

This success of Caesar's inconvenienced the townsfolk to a very great extent, but it did not drive them to desperation because as it happened three hundred feet up from the river a spring gushed forth close under the walls of the town and made its way down to the river with the usual headlong speed of a mountain stream. It was not so easy for cattle to be watered here, but by taking trouble, men were able to fill what buckets they pleased. This sufficed.

Caesar now crossed the stream and began to build a ramp up the hill, protecting his workmen with sheds in the traditional fashion. Owing, however, to the slope of the ground, this was hard and dangerous work. It was easy for the townsmen to stand a little too high on the slope for us to reach and to shower our men with missiles which we could not return. Many of us were wounded, and our progress was slow. Gradually we began to inch forward and upward. After great struggles we had built our ramp forty feet high and had erected at the end of it a wooden tower of ten stories. This by no means overlooked the walls of the town, which were far too high for

any possible structure to be brought up against them. It
did, however, command the source of the stream so that
we were able to mount a catapult and make it dangerous
for the townspeople to draw any water at all.

Now indeed they began to suffer from thirst. We
could hear the bellowing of their frantic cattle and watch
their despairing efforts to fill their vessels at the spring and
escape thence with life. It seemed most probable that they
would have to give up to us, but they did not. In Uxellodunum there were desperate men from all over Gaul, and
no privation which we could inflict on them was worse
than surrender.

In desperation, the enemy filled many casks with tal-
low, pitch, and shingles, set them on fire, and rolled them
down upon us. A great flame shot up in our siegeworks,
while the townsfolk made a sortie in force to prevent our
putting it out. Since they were again able to pelt us with
weapons from afar, and since our people were bound to
expose themselves in putting out the flames, our casualties
were heavy. In fact Caesar began to fear lest all our work
be lost and, still more disastrously, lest they drive us back
and discover what we had been doing. For under cover
of working on the ramp and the tower, Caesar had mining
parties tunneling right up the hill in hopes of finding the
sources of the spring and cutting it off. Hastily he ordered his forces to ascend the hill on every side and to raise
a shout as though they were assaulting the town. They
could not have done so, yet perhaps our reputation saved
us. All knew how often our troops had achieved what
seemed impossible. At all events the townsfolk drew off
in the nick of time, and we quenched the flame.

After that the siege went on, though people were
literally dying of thirst in the town and though the ap-

proaches to the spring were horribly strewn with unburied
corpses. Not even the people of Alesia had resisted in this
way, though they had threatened to feed on one another's
flesh and had actually driven noncombatants outside to
perish. In Uxellodunum, women and children lay dead by
the spring as well as men and even skirmished with us as
far as they dared, protecting their weakness by use of the
higher ground. No hope of rescue, hardly even hope of
survival sustained them. They fought till they died.

This might have gone on all the summer till the whole
garrison lay dead about the spring and there was no one to
drag a corpse away and stoop to the water. It might have
gone on, as Caesar feared, until some other madman took
heart — Lucterius perhaps, or even Commius, still exer-
cising the magic of his persuasion on the Germans. Fortunately for us, our underground miners came on the
source of the spring and diverted it. With dramatic sud-
denness, the perilous water ceased to flow.

I believe even then that the people of Uxellodunum
might have killed themselves or sallied forth to die fighting
if they had known what we had done. But perceiving their
perpetual spring go suddenly dry, they thought it a miracle and concluded that the gods had abandoned them.
They surrendered to Caesar.

They might have been wiser to have died. Caesar was
not naturally cruel. Indeed, like many a soldier, he de-
tested suffering caused in cold blood, though the horrors
of battle affected him hardly at all. Yet though the taste
of cruelty was evil in his mouth, he did not shrink from
it any more than he did from cold or hunger or hardship
when he found these necessary to be endured. Because
of this quality in him, he was more to be feared at times
than crueler people. Others might be diverted from their

vengeance by whim, satiety, or even by other offenders.
Not so Caesar. Having made up his mind to punish for
reasons which seemed good, he always did so. Wrapping
himself in a bitter, cold, sarcastic, distant mood, he seemed
impervious to prayers, screams, tears, entreaties. People
wondered that a man who forgave so readily could be so
savage.

Perhaps from the very time he came to Uxellodunum,
Caesar had determined he must make an example here.
The stubborn resistance prolonged to its hopeless end
had merely confirmed him in his intention. There could
be no profit either to himself or to Gaul in forgiving men
who would continue to hate. Better be ruthless here and
save his mercy for those from whom he might expect
obedience. On this occasion, it would not be enough to
put these men to death. He had waded in rivers of blood,
and still these bands of brigands rose and would rise as
long as they dared. He would show them that the risks
were not worth taking, once and for all.

Thus Caesar reasoned, and doing so was pitiless. The
wretched defenders of Uxellodunum all had their hands
cut off and were turned away to subsist, if they could,
on the compassion of their neighbors while they served
as a dreadful example to all Gaul. This last fearful act
served its purpose. War was over.

There remained two irreconcilables, Lucterius hiding
out in the Arvernian country and Commius in the
north. Their fates were very different. Among the Arvernians and their neighboring tribes, Lucterius had been
loved. Many people, though they submitted to Caesar,
were willing to hide him. Among these, Lucterius moved
for a while, trusting perforce to the honor of many, lest
rumor reveal his presence in any one spot. There was a

price on his head, and before long one of his former friends betrayed him. Lucterius vanished from the sight of men into that living death where Vercingetorix awaited Caesar's triumph and the end.

Meanwhile Commius had returned across the Rhine without the Germans, finding after Uxellodunum that there were limits even to his powers of persuasion. His people had submitted to Caesar, and his kingship over them was not considered valid any longer. Commius, however, had with him a retinue of some size and was hard to ignore. He made attempts to talk his neighbors into renewing the war, but had little success. In fact, insensibly his own men began to drift away until in desperation he took to brigandage to support them. By the time the Romans went into winter quarters at the end of 51, Commius had established himself in sufficient strength to be a nuisance.

It was Mark Antony who was quartered in that region, and he had with him Gaius Volusenus, who had by now been promoted to prefect of his cavalry. Volusenus's hatred for Commius had not by any means decreased with time. In fact, I rather think that Commius's refusal to be quite murdered had merely added to his original grievance. It was no coincidence that Volusenus had been quartered with Antony, for he had himself requested the assignment.

It seems quite possible that Antony felt, as most of us did, that Volusenus was unreasonable about Commius. It is probable also in view of what happened later that he had spoken with Caesar on the subject. Antony was becoming intimate with Caesar, while on the other hand he was more than a little cool towards Labienus.

For these or other reasons, Antony at first left Commius

alone. He, however, lost no time in transferring his attentions from his neighbors to the Romans. After he had managed to ambush no less than three convoys of supplies, it had become obvious to Antony that he would have to be dealt with.

Volusenus was jubilant. In fact he did not scruple to remind Antony that he had told him so, a piece of imprudence which our growing concern with the future made unwise. Still, Volusenus was high in favor with Caesar also, for though he was hardly well born enough to be used as Legate, he had real capacity for command. On this occasion, he went to work systematically. Volusenus had his own methods of extracting information from Gauls. Perhaps few of our ways were pleasant ones, but his were more unsavory than most. He had little trouble in finding out where Commius lurked and in laying an ambush.

Commius fell into the trap. No doubt it was not always easy for him to find out all he wished, since the Atrebates on the whole desired to be left in peace and would have been glad to be rid of him. Volusenus, attacking him suddenly from both sides, put his men to flight with ease. Commius fled with them, and Volusenus with a small band of attendants followed after, eager to finish the killing which he had begun two years before. Pursued and pursuers thundered down a winding valley by the banks of a little stream, one side gaining and then the other, according to the nature of the ground. Volusenus, urging his horse in the front rank, was shouting after Commius, for he feared lest his helmet conceal from the chief who it was that followed so closely.

Commius was riding as though for his life, looking back anxiously over his shoulder from time to time and measur-

ing his distance. Commius, however, was no ordinary
Gaul. Though defeated, though escaping with a small
remnant of his band, though pursued by his deadly enemy,
he kept his head. When he had drawn Volusenus away
from the main body of his men, he cried to his own escort
to stand with him and fight. The band of Romans which
pursued them was fewer in numbers than they were themselves. His honor demanded that the treacherous wound
which had nearly killed him should be avenged.

Thus shouting, he turned his horse and rode at the Romans, his men surging after. Volusenus, whose rage had
blinded him to his danger, was swept back with his men.
The Romans wheeled their horses and in their turn tried
to escape. Commius, however, bursting into their midst
like a thunderbolt, thrust at Volusenus with such strength
that his spear tore clean through the shield and through
Volusenus's thigh. Had not the soldiers rallied desperately to protect their prefect, and if reinforcements had
not come up, Volusenus would certainly have been a dead
man. As it was, after a fierce skirmish in which many of
the Gauls were killed, Commius once more escaped by
flight. As for Volusenus, he was carried back to camp and
lay long in peril of his life.

Evidently Commius felt his honor satisfied, for he sent
to Antony to treat for peace. No doubt, being Commius,
he was also influenced by the fact that his supporters were
now few in number. At all events, he sent an envoy, of-
fering hostages and promising to go away and live in peace.
He requested, however, that in deference to his vow and
to the treatment he had already received he be permitted
to leave without being forced to meet any Roman. This
Antony with Caesar's consent allowed, and that he did
so was Caesar's only public comment on Labienus, who

had permitted the act of treachery. What he had said to him in private, I do not know. For several reasons, Labienus and he were seen to be no longer on intimate terms.

Commius went his way and crossed to Britain, where he could easily keep his oath to look on no Roman. Arriving as he did a discredited leader, almost alone, he managed in the course of a very few years to make himself king. No doubt he persuaded the chiefs of those parts one by one, his hand on their shoulders. Eventually Commius's kingdom rivaled even that of the great British king, Cassivellaunus. So securely was it founded that when he died full of years, it passed to his sons. Thus Commius never again looked on a Roman.

EPILOGUE

The Gallic war was over. Gauls were discovering from a year of quiet rule that Caesar's government imposed little on them save peace with one another and a tribute which they might raise in their own way. Italian traders and sharp commercial men who had followed the armies for so long were now everywhere. Money-making for its own sake was new to the Gauls, but the spirit of intrigue and the ambition had always been present. A fresh atmosphere, a new outlet for energy was being presented. Gaul would still breed fighters, but Roman civilization would blossom like a flower transplanted to virgin soil. Roman Gaul had a future.

Meanwhile, the Roman legionaries had achieved what

they were fighting for. Little Varus of the Twelfth was twenty-three by now and standard-bearer of his cohort. What with plunder, pay, and bonuses from Caesar, he ought to have been quite rich. The traders had cheated him out of a great deal, and he had contracted a habit of gambling which had made away with most of the rest. He possessed, however, silver plaques attached to his armor which he wore in part for display, in part because the riches one regularly had on one's person could not be stolen. For the rest, Caesar had recently doubled his pay. What would happen if the army were to be disbanded, he did not consider. In any case, most of his officers appeared to think there would be civil war. This did not disturb Varus, since he was not Roman but Italian and had in any case not much attachment to home. He belonged to his legion.

Sextius Baculus was semi-retired. After his last wounds he developed a limp which made it impossible for him to keep up on the march. After all these years as centurion, his savings were large enough for a respectable farm and a group of slaves. Baculus, however, had stayed to join the veterans who were allowed to ride instead of marching. There was talk of Caesar's trying him out for a new position called Camp Prefect with wide administrative duties. Baculus was forty, and he reckoned he could have at least fifteen more years with the legions.

I myself was in Narbonese Gaul, recovering slowly from a spear thrust in the ribs and a broken leg. I, too, had gained modest wealth in Gaul, though it has done me little good without my health. But though that spear thrust wrecked my life, it also saved it. Volusenus, young Marcellus, Antony, Cicero, Labienus, nearly all the men who fought beside me were killed in the civil war. I only survived it because my ambitions were gone and my fighting days over.

Caesar, meanwhile, was at Ravenna, waiting to see what happened at Rome. He had gained enormously from the war, but all of this by itself was as nothing. Wealth, reputation, armies were but means to an end. He belonged to a circle to whom power at Rome was the only possible aim of human ambition. Caesar had pondered the anarchy at Rome, the political corruption, the tyranny of murderous gangs, the inability of the old regime to cope with modern conditions. He intended if he became consul to make a clean sweep. He knew the conservatives were employing fair means and foul to prevent him from ever attaining this office. If the Senate resorted to actual force, he would make war.

Thus Caesar waited, writing reasonable letters, proposing compromises which satisfied no one. The Senate understood the extent of his ambition and would not endure to be set aside. Yet the majority of its members dreaded war.

Pompey the Great, as he liked to be called, had put on weight with middle age, and his pompous silences had grown into a way of concealing his opinion. He had married again quite happily and forgotten Julia. In speaking of Caesar, he was careful to be polite; yet he liked to have it understood that Gallic savages were easy prey compared to the opponents whom he himself had overcome. He was both jealous and rather contemptuous of Caesar's achievement.

Roman government had reached such a pitch of anarchy that it could not be carried on save under the protection of a strong man who could use his troops as police. Pompey was such a man, and from the conservative point of view a safe one because he merely wanted to be the exception to all rules, not to change them as Caesar did. In this way Pompey had become sole consul. He still governed

Spain from Rome and maintained legions there. He had two more legions in southern Italy, which he had collected under pretext of going east against the Parthians. In similar fashion, he disposed of legions in North Africa. He felt stronger than Caesar, and under constant prodding by extreme conservatives, he had made up his mind to fight.

Once Pompey had resolved, the Senate could be stampeded. In spite of the reluctance of many, it proclaimed martial law, which would allow it to set aside by force those who supported Caesar's cause in Rome. This was in January, 49. On the eleventh of that month Caesar was over the border of his province into Italy and had seized Rimini. He had been forced into war, as he was careful to point out, by the action of the Senate. What Caesar did not say was that this war had been in preparation ever since that day nearly nine years ago when he and I had pounded up the Aemilian Way towards his province. He had gone to Gaul to raise an army and train it. He had always intended to use it for counterbalancing Pompey and to gain power in Rome. He had hoped, no doubt, to avoid a war; yet he had chosen one by his own course from the first. He expected to win it.

Place names used in the text	Their Roman equivalents
Alesia	Alesia
Amiens	Samarobriva
Besançon	Vesontio
Bibracte	Bibrax
Boulogne	Itium
Bourges	Avaricum
Garonne River	Garumna
Geneva	Genava
Gergovia	Gergovia
Langres	Territory of the Lingones
Loire River	Liger
Marseilles	Massilia
Meuse River	Mosa
Narbonne	Narbo
Nevers	Noviodunum
Orléans	Cenabum
Paris	Lutetia
Poitiers	Lemonum
Rhine River	Rhenus
Rhone River	Rhodanus
Sambre River	Sabis
Saône River	Arar
Seine River	Sequana
Sens	Agedincum
Uxellodunum	Uxellodunum
Vienne	Vienna